Ecology of Populations

Ecology of Populations

ARTHUR S. BOUGHEY

University of California Irvine

SECOND EDITION

The Macmillan Company, New York
Collier-Macmillan Publishers, London

The Macmillan Company
866 Third Avenue, New York, New York 10022

Collier-Macmillan Canada, Ltd., Toronto, Ontario

Library of Congress catalog card number: 72-84739

Printing: 1 2 3 4 5 6 7 8   Year: 3 4 5 6 7 8 9

Preface

Ecology is a young science; its aims and objects have become clearly discernible only during the last decade. Previously it was a somewhat diffuse and uncoordinated discipline, struggling to embrace field studies in such areas as physiology, genetics, and evolution and to relate them within the framework of the anecdotal phase of natural history. Because of the original subdivision of living systems into either plants or animals, the new ecological studies were initially undertaken by botanists or zoologists. The former inclined to assume a holistic view of their subject and to engage in what were subsequently called *synecological* investigations. The latter adopted a meristic viewpoint and proceeded along lines that came to be known as *autecological*. Although now difficult to maintain in a research approach, the retention of this historical subdivision of ecology still has some pedagogical convenience.

This present volume considers the primarily *autecological* phenomena of population ecology. The companion volume, on communities and ecosystems, embraces essentially their synecological aspects. Separated in this way, autecology and synecology represent two successive levels of biological organization. Their separation emphasizes that the ecology of populations is in one sense different from the ecology of communities. Although there are no features of populations that cannot be identified again in communities, the reverse does not hold. Communities have certain unique features like species diversity, successional stages, and energetics interrelationships, which populations cannot show. At the same time, populations exhibit certain features like growth, which, although they do persist into the community level, are nevertheless more difficult to investigate there. Although autecology has now advanced far beyond the simple cause-effect investigations of a previous generation of ecologists, analytical techniques are not yet so sophisticated as to permit a full factorial analysis of population contributions within complex ecosystems.

There is a second reason why autecological studies can still be actively and profitably pursued. Recent technological developments have immensely refined many aspects of telemetering and remote sensing. Partly as a spin-off from the space program, the miniaturization of various electronic devices as a result of the application of solid-state physics has produced sensing, recording, and transmitting devices small enough for application on the bodies or insertion into the tissues of a great range of plants and animals. Signals on multichannel recorders can be received from such microtransmitters from considerable distances, and even from earth satellites. These technological improvements have invigorated studies in physiology and behavior. Such studies have been still further stimulated by the possibilities that now exist for the modeling of these processes using analog and digital computers.

The general availability of third-generation and perhaps soon fourth-generation computers, associated with the systems approach, has, however, had an even more fundamental effect than this on autecology. It has instigated a change of emphasis from the various ecological characteristics of particular populations to the nature of the interactions between them. This emphasis on population interactions, moreover, has been reinforced by a general application of the chemical microanalytical techniques of chromatography and electrophoresis to the investigation of allelochemical interactions. Although much time and effort is currently being expended on community studies of energetics and nutrient cycling, interest is also deepening in the area of population interactions. Indeed, in order to understand the one, it is essential to investigate the other.

It is this modeling activity in ecology, and its essential preliminary, systems analysis, that makes the current presentation of any introductory survey text on autecology very difficult. Autecological situations are now approached by systems analysis and model construction, which separates the problem into as many hypothetical iterative stages as may initially be identified. From the interpretation of this phase, a stochastic simulation model can be developed. Finally, this model is refined by testing, with a different set of criteria, against a real world system. It is relatively easy to describe the current autecological investigations that are proceeding along these lines. Excellent works such as those edited by K. E. F. Watt and B. C. Patten have already done so. What is mostly revealed by such compilations, however, is ecological methodologies rather than ecological concepts. These emerge but slowly from the continuing synthesis of ideas drawn from many successful model-verification operations. A particular concept rarely finds general acceptance until these verifications reach, as it were, a critical mass. In synecology, it is possible that the immense activity in the investigation of ecosystem bio-energetics has reached this critical mass stage. In autecology it is very apparent that is has, in general, not yet done so. The basic autecological concepts that we currently utilize are those fashioned in a previous time by different methods; those that we retain have survived testing and have even been substantiated by the new approach.

This second edition incorporates more extensive reference to these new autecological procedures, and also emphasizes their extensive application to boundary and interactive phenomena. It also incorporates one further major change. Since the publication of the first edition, the nature and extent of current environmental crises have finally begun to be realized. It has become apparent that problems of environmental management that require the application of the basic principles of community ecology cannot be resolved without a more complete understanding of human behavior. One of the major tasks of the new ecology is to embark upon the autecological investigation of the behavior of our own species. To do so we must draw upon our growing knowledge of behavior as a whole. This forms the topic of a fresh chapter. This edition, like the original one, also considers such matters in a concluding chapter on human ecology.

This revised volume is therefore intended, as was the original, for the beginning student in ecology, and it assumes no greater an acquaintance with biology than would be obtained from a high school or college survey course. It explains, explores, and illustrates the principal current concepts of population ecology and describes the main directions in which autecological theory is now proceeding. The short bibliographical lists at the end of each chapter include source material referring to the ecological ideas presented in the chapter. They also include some original papers dealing with the particular topics at an appropriate introductory level. These further readings enable the student to become more familiar with the various concepts and to explore further the experimental and observational evidence on which they are based. The seven chapters, somewhat expanded and slightly rearranged, follow a progressive pattern from population characteristics, through their environmental and biotic interactions, to their organization into communities. The text inevitably touches on some aspects of the subject matter of other volumes in this series; their titles are listed in appropriate chapter bibliographies. Further information on these interdisciplinary aspects of ecology may be obtained from these other works.

I am grateful to the many students in various countries who have listened critically, but on the whole patiently, to my evolving accounts of ecology; by their reactions these students have helped to develop my ideas. Especially I must thank my colleague George Hunt for constructive criticism of Chapter 5 and James Pick for his review of the first chapter.

My appreciation must also be recorded for the continuing assistance received from my former colleague Robert Whittaker, the author of the companion work on community ecology in this series.

A. S. Boughey

University of California Irvine

Contents

Chapter 1 • Population Characteristics

The living world is composed of systems at different levels of biological organization. These range from molecular intracellular structures through organelles, cells, tissues, organs, and organisms to the largest and most complex arrangements in populations and communities. At all these levels of biological organization these living systems interact with their environment; at none of them can these environmental interactions be ignored. It is, however, at their most complex level that we have most emphasized such cybernetic processes and have formally incorporated them in the ecosystem concept. At the population level also, where until recently these environmental interactions had been most extensively studied, environmental influences have similarly received considerable emphasis. Thus although we commonly define *ecology* as the study of populations and communities and their interrelationships with one another and with their environment, it must not be forgotten that living systems at all levels of biological organization likewise have environmental interactions.

The declared intent of this text is to explore the ecology of populations, that is, the nature of populations and their interactions with one another and with their total environment. The term *population* is used in many ways and can have as many different meanings. For the purposes of this text it is generally taken to be a *species population*. This may be defined as an assemblage of organisms with a considerable number of characteristics in common, a similar origin, and no barriers that prevent individual members' freely interbreeding with one another when heterosexual individuals are brought together.

Defined in this way, the populations of this planet have been estimated to comprise some 5 million plant species, 10 million animal species, and perhaps 2 or 3 million species of microorganisms. Of these some 10 per cent of plants and animals and perhaps 5 per cent of microorganisms have already been described and named. The destructive effects of our burgeoning industrial organizations are now having such a disastrous impact on wild populations that many of these may well become extinct before their presence is scientifically recorded. Like many of the ancestral forms of our own species, we shall only be able to speculate as to their one-time existence.

The populations that we have so far scientifically recognized exhibit characteristics that fall initially into two groups. First, there are those that are shared in common with all lower levels of biological organization; then there are the unique features that characterize populations alone. As with every subordinate organizational level, these are unique only as regards subordinate levels; these unique population features, albeit modified, are also encountered in the level of biological organization above populations, that is, communities. This level alone shows truly unique features. How these develop from populations is the topic of one of the final chapters in this text.

This first chapter explores the intrinsic characteristics of populations. The diagnostic features used to define living matter are *growth, response,* and *reproduction.* A population can be defined on the same basis. Just as living matter must exhibit growth and response and commonly undergo reproduction, individual organisms grow and respond and usually beget an assemblage of descendants that together form what is defined here as a *population.*

The distinctive biological characteristics of individual organisms are also inherent in the population. As the individual organism grows, reproduces, and responds to the environment, so does the population. Over and beyond these common characteristics, however, are features inherent in sociality, such as birth rates and death rates, survivorship and age structure. These a population exhibits uniquely by virtue of its collective nature. The population ecologist is thus concerned essentially with the definition, origin, occurrence, abundance, dispersal, behavior, and interactions of species populations. This first chapter deals more particularly with what may be called the *dynamic* features of the population, such as growth and regulation, periodicity and stabilization, reproduction and territoriality.

Population Growth

Of the several dynamic features that a population displays, the most fundamental is that of *growth,* the capacity for increase in individual numbers. Indeed, growth as so defined is one of the essential characteristics that helps differentiate between a living population and dead material of organic origin.

The *rate of growth* of a population is expressed as the number of individuals by which the population increases divided by the amount of time that elapses while this population increase is taking place. The growth rate of a population may be represented as

$$\frac{\Delta N}{\Delta t} \tag{1-1}$$

where

N = the initial number of individuals in the population
Δ = the extent of change
t = time

Thus, ΔN represents any change in the number of individuals in a population, and Δt, the time interval for this change.

Rate of Growth

If we are dealing with a population that is not gaining or losing individual members by migration, such a change in size if it is positive can only be achieved by the addition of offspring. That is, births or *natality* must occur. There are several ways in which natality can be estimated. It is always, however, modified to the extent that any deaths or *mortality* is simultaneously occurring.

Exponential Growth

It is possible to express population increases as measured by the difference between natality and mortality instantaneously. Then ΔN in Equation 1-1 becomes dN, and Δt, dt, the amount of change in a moment of time. The rate of population increase is then

$$\frac{dN}{dt}$$

As this is registered by the amount of natality (B) from which has been subtracted the extent of mortality (D), it follows that

$$\frac{\Delta N}{\Delta t} = B - D \tag{1-2}$$

However, the sizes of B and D are dependent on the size of the population (N) and must be related to it. So written algebraically

$$B = bN \quad \text{and} \quad D = dN$$

Written algebraically Equation 1-2 for population increase then becomes

$$\frac{\Delta N}{\Delta t} = bN - dN \tag{1-3}$$

or more simply

$$\frac{\Delta N}{\Delta t} = (b - d)N \tag{1-4}$$

In practice $(b - d)$ is usually replaced by the constant r, the *intrinsic rate of increase*. Equation 1-4 may thus be written

$$\frac{\Delta N}{\Delta t} = rN$$

The equivalent instantaneous expression is

$$\frac{dN}{dt} = rN \tag{1-5}$$

Plotted as an arithmetical expression this gives the so-called J-shaped form of population growth of line A illustrated in Figure 1-1. When a logarithmic value is substituted for the arithmetical value, this relationship becomes a straight line as indicated by line B in Figure 1-1. The slope of this line expresses the value of r; any positive value of this rate of increase produces *exponential population growth*. If d is greater than b, r will have a negative value, i.e., the population density will be *decreasing*. If this situation continues it will lead to extinction.

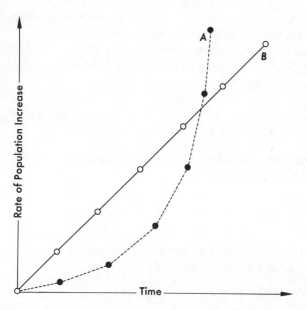

Figure 1-1. Exponential growth. Theoretical figures plotting time (horizontal coordinate) against the rate of population increase (vertical coordinate). The dotted line A is an arithmetic expression of the rate of increase, and the solid line B, the logarithmic expression. Note the J-shaped curve of A and the straight-line relationship of B.

Populations such as bacteria or amoebae in which each organism divides into daughter organisms possess a simply fantastic capacity for growth while conditions remain favorable, that is, while an exponential growth rate can continue. A bacterium dividing every twenty minutes would, as described by R. H. MacArthur and J. H. Connell, produce a colony one foot deep over the entire earth in a day and a half. One hour later, the layer of bacteria would be over our heads. At this theoretical rate of growth, within a few thousand years any plant or animal population would weigh as much as the visible universe and would be expanding outward at the speed of light.

Under theoretically ideal conditions, when there are no restricting factors imposed by the physical or biotic environment, a population could be considered capable of exhibiting a *maximum intrinsic rate of increase.* This ability of a population to grow maximally and exponentially is known classically as the *biotic potential.* It is characteristic of that population when it is allowed to develop in an optimal environment of unlimited extent. The biotic potential is, however, almost always an indication of a theoretical rate of growth, not an actual one. This is expressed by the *realized intrinsic rate of increase.* For example, a whale population may have a lower biotic potential than an amoeba species population, but it is highly probable that under natural conditions, in both of them the natality rate equals the mortality rate and the population size remains constant about a mean. Thus the biotic potential is checked under natural circumstances as it eventually is under cultural conditions. This check is imposed by *environmental resistance,* which exists when some factor, or factors, of the environment becomes limiting and decreases the natality rate, increases the mortality rate, or does both.

The limit imposed by environmental resistance is represented by the symbol K. Inserting this constant into the expression for the rate of growth previously developed provides the simple logistic model.

$$\frac{dN}{dt} = rN\frac{(K - N)}{K} \qquad (1\text{-}6)$$

This limit to the biotic potential of a population imposed at a particular population size by environmental resistance under a given set of conditions is most generally known as its *carrying capacity.* Commonly such a limit is imposed by exhaustion of either food supplies or space. The sudden imposition of a carrying-capacity limit may result in the J-shaped curve of the biotic potential's falling away abruptly. Sometimes, and especially if the carrying capacity is determined by food supply, the population *overshoots* and temporarily exhausts all available supplies; then the population *crashes* (Figure 1-2). Frequently in this form of increase, population numbers decline and then temporarily build again in an oscillating pattern (Figure 1-3), as they may do even following a

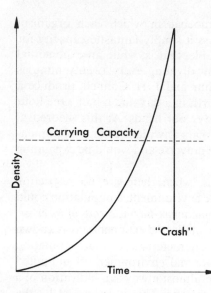

Figure 1-2. A theoretical example of population increase that has overshot the carrying capacity, with a resultant crash.

crash. Such behavior is characteristic of some insect and most annual-plant populations.

The relationship between the biotic potential, the population growth curve, and environmental resistance is shown in Figure 1-4. The growth of many species populations of animals, plants, and microorganisms follows this sigmoid pattern, but it must not be assumed that the growth of these populations is entirely represented by the logistic equation, for numerous mathematical equations can produce a sigmoid curve. Populations in laboratory experiments and lower organisms such as bacteria and yeasts appear to have a linear increase with density in the region of the

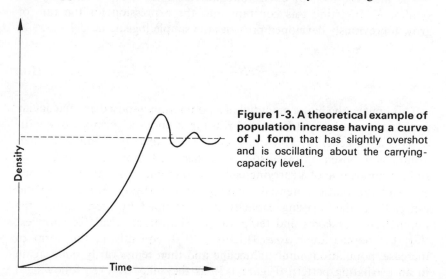

Figure 1-3. A theoretical example of population increase having a curve of J form that has slightly overshot and is oscillating about the carrying-capacity level.

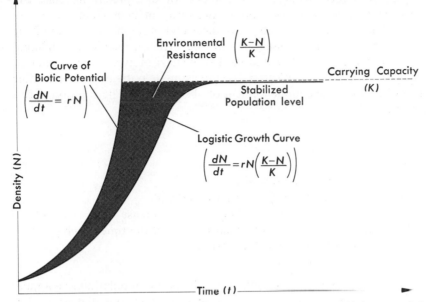

Figure 1-4. Diagram of the theoretical relationships between biotic potential, logistic growth, and environmental resistance.

curve where environmental resistance is first encountered. Some birds and mammals have a similar relationship. As an example of this, E. P. Odum uses the population growth of sheep when they were introduced for the first time into the island of Tasmania near the beginning of the nineteenth century (Figure 1-5). By plotting the growth of the sheep population from the figures that were kept, it can be seen that the asymptote of some 1.7 million sheep was reached about the middle of the century.

The environmental resistance that eventually causes a leveling off of the rate of population increase in logistic growth commonly arises from

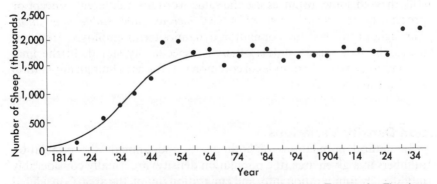

Figure 1-5. Population growth of sheep introduced into Tasmania. The dots represent average numbers over five-year periods. From J. Davidson, *Transactions of the Royal Society of South Australia,* 62:342–346 (1938).

two forms of species interaction: competition and predation. These are considered briefly here and more extensively in later chapters. Before proceeding to examine the effects of these and other factors in modifying rates of increase, it is necessary to note one further principle. The differential Equation 1-5 can be solved so that, instead of expressing the rate of change in a population, it can be used to estimate population size at some time other than the commencement of observations. The solution of this equation is

$$N = N_o e^{rt}$$

where

    N_o = the initial population size
    e = the base of natural logarithms 2.718628
    r = the instantaneous rate of population increase
    t = unit of time of measurement of N_o and the time at which the population estimate N is desired

As will be apparent, this method of calculating population size applies only to examples where the rate of growth is exponential. It is thus essentially a theoretical consideration with limited application to natural populations.

Human Demography

Studies on the growth of populations as described in this chapter may be labeled *population dynamics* or *demography*. The conclusions drawn from such studies may be applied to all populations, including our own. Unfortunately human demographic studies have generally proceeded without reference to the population dynamics of any other species. Consequently we currently have two sets of demographic terms. Worse still, these in some instances use the same word for a different concept or process, as in *intrinsic rate of natural increase* and *stable population*. Throughout this text the population dynamics terms employed are those for nonhuman species unless otherwise specifically stated. In the final chapter some typical examples of common variations in human population structure are considered.

Population Density Variations

In natural populations of both plants and animals the population numbers in a given area (the population density) are usually considerably modified by immigration into, and emigration out of, the area. Considered in terms of population dynamics, this complication will have rather similar effects to increasing the birth rate, and increasing the mortality rate, respectively. Even when this modification is taken into account, however, single-species populations are found not only to differ considerably from one another in numbers of individuals, but also to have finite densities. One of the major controversies in population ecology is over the nature of the factors that determine the level of numbers in, or *regulate,* a given population. The classic work by H. G. Andrewartha and L. C. Birch represents one side of the controversy. These authors deal especially with populations, often insects, that are limited not by the food supply but by the physical environment. Such a population is represented, for example, by adult thrips, whose seasonal changes in numbers are illustrated in Figure 1-6. Given a knowledge of local meteorology, the rate of mobility of the thrips, the distance from an existing thrips population, and the intrinsic rate of increase, a forecast may be made of the number that will occur in any one space at any time. (However, it must be noted that F. E. Smith challenged certain parts of this work.)

By contrast, the large animals of the Tropical and Frigid Zones are not usually limited in numbers by the physical environment. Elephants, most inefficient metabolizers, increase when poaching and shooting are eliminated and water supplies are plentiful until their great food consumption can entirely destroy their habitat. At the other end of the climatic scale, polar bears in the North Frigid Zone are challenged, not by the cold, but by their inability to obtain food. In both these cases food can be the factor limiting population numbers. Numerous such cases have been discussed by D. Lack, and a theoretical consideration is provided by Wilson and Bossert, as will be discussed shortly.

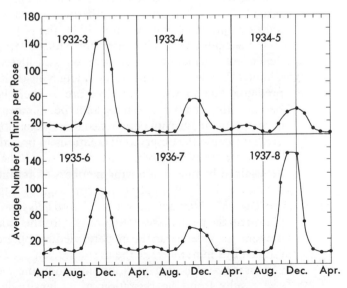

Figure 1-6. Seasonal changes in a population of adult thrips living on rose bushes. Reprinted from *The Distribution and Abundance of Animals* by H. G. Andrewartha and L. C. Birch by permission of The University of Chicago Press. Copyright 1954 by The University of Chicago Press.

Density Dependence and Density Independence

These two contrasting approaches to regulation of animal numbers have been called respectively the *density-independent* and *density-dependent* viewpoints. Andrewartha and Birch were especially concerned with insects, Lack with birds; the possibility that this circumstance may explain their apparently opposing arguments has been discussed by G. H. Orians. He considers that the argument centers around a fundamental division of modern biology into functional biology and evolutionary biology. As functional ecologists, Andrewartha and Birch are concerned with the operation and interaction of populations; they have as a major concern the experimental control of environmental variables, leading to the rejection of results based on the action of natural selection on populations. Evolutionary ecologists such as Lack, Orians suggests, are primarily concerned with the causes behind observable ecological adaptations. For example, in the evolution of reproductive rates (an adaptation), climate can be ignored as a significant regulating factor. It is a question of *proximate* and *ultimate* factors; functional ecologists deal with the first, the *immediate* environmental effects. Evolutionary ecologists are concerned with the second, the longer term influences exerted on successive generations of a population.

By contrast with animal populations, plant populations have until recently been little investigated by the population ecologist. J. L. Harper and his co-workers have pioneered investigations of plant populations at the seedling stage. Harper maintains that although it is commonly argued that the regulation of density must be by density-dependent processes, in many seed germination experiments that he conducted the number of individuals that became established was a direct function of the safe microsites provided on the soil surface. In other words, maximum population size in plants could be determined directly by the physical environment.

The predator-prey relationship provides a typical example of density-dependent regulation which will be considered more extensively in Chapter 4. Figure 1-7 illustrates changes in the abundance of lynx (the predator) and snowshoe hare (the prey). There is a positive correlation between the number of lynxes and the number of hares, as might be expected, but it must not be assumed that fluctuations in the numbers of the predator cause the observed fluctuations in prey density.

Parasites provide another instance in which the size of a population is determined by interaction with members of another population. S. Utida illustrated this by fluctuating numbers of a host, the bean weevil *Callosobrochus chinensis,* and a wasp, *Heterospilus prosopidis,* whose larvae parasitize the weevil larvae (Figure 1-8). In this example also, fluctuations in numbers of the parasites are paralleled by, but not precisely reflected in, fluctuations in numbers of the host.

A more complicated situation, in which the regulation of population size results from the operation of a density-dependent factor, is the

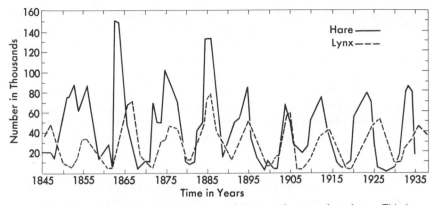

Figure 1-7. Changes in the abundance of lynx and snowshoe hare. This is a classic example of the cyclic oscillation in population density and illustrates the correlation between fluctuations in numbers of prey (hare) and numbers of predator (lynx). After D. A. MacLulich, *University of Toronto Studies, Biological Series No. 43,* 1937, pp. 1–136.

phenomenon known as *territoriality*. This is a very common characteristic of many animal populations and is further discussed in Chapter 5. Like a number of other regulatory behavioral mechanisms, territoriality has most extensively been investigated in respect to birds. In this group

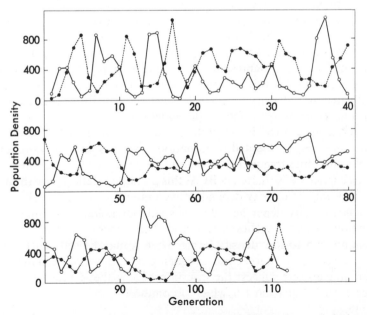

Figure 1-8. Fluctuation in population density of interacting populations of a host, the bean weevil *Callosobruchus chinensis* (solid line) and a parasite, the abracenid wasp *Heterospilus prosopidis* (broken line). [From S. Utida, *Ecology,* 38:442–449 (1957).

generally, individual males in the breeding season occupy a territory whose boundaries are marked by displays, often in the form of birdsong. Other males are driven out of this territory, so are other females unless they are the one or ones which have mated with that particular male. This system maintains a pool of unmated birds of a size that varies from year to year with the carrying capacity of the habitat. In a good year, territories can be smaller but still provide the same yield of food; there will be fewer unmated birds, and a greater production of young. A typical example of this regulatory mechanism has been described by Watson and Jenkins (1968).

If growth in a population were to be controlled entirely by density-independent factors it would probably not long survive. Such a population would fluctuate in size upward and downward about its carrying capacity (K), according to the operation of the density-independent factors controlling it. When it moved downward there would be no compensatory density-dependent mechanisms to slow down its decline in numbers. During such periods of adverse values of the density-independent factors, the population might well face local if not total extinction. It appears likely that all natural populations have compensatory density-dependent mechanisms that buffer them from such disastrous declines in population size.

Many examples of density-dependent regulation of populations have been described. The situation may be illustrated generally and graphically as in Figure 1-9. As represented in Figure 1-9 **A,** birth rates in a population reproducing under the influence of a density-independent factor will remain constant whatever the population size. By contrast, a density-dependent factor will depress the birth rate as population density rises. Likewise, death rates will remain constant if population density is under the influence of a density-independent factor but will rise (Figure 1-9 **A**) when it is regulated by a density-dependent one.

However, as growth in naturally occurring populations follows the logistic curve as represented in Equation 1-6, at some high value of N, d eventually comes to equal b. This point, as has been seen, represents the carrying capacity K (Figure 1-9 **B**). At this point population growth can be controlled only by density-dependent factors.

Actually, density-dependent effects usually intervene some time before population density reaches this point. They operate especially when populations fall to low density levels. Then it may be difficult to avoid deleterious effects from too close inbreeding, or even to locate mates at all. Wilson and Bossert suggest the insertion of a further factor M into the logistic growth Equation 1-6, which becomes

$$\frac{dN}{dt} = rN\left(\frac{K - N}{K}\right)\left(\frac{N - M}{N}\right) \tag{1-7}$$

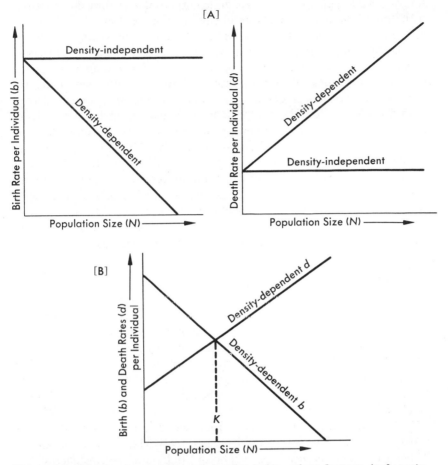

Figure 1-9. Density-dependent and density-independent factors. In **A**, as the population density increases, the birth rate (*b*) falls under the influence of a density-dependent factor, while it remains constant with a density-independent one. Similarly mortality (*d*) rises in the first case and remains constant in the second.

A stable population can be achieved only at the point where a rising mortality (*d*) intersects a falling natality (*b*) as in **B**, provided density-dependent factors are operating. Where *b* and *d* intersect is the population size (*N*) at the carrying capacity (*K*) under the conditions specified. If mortality and natality are controlled by density-independent factors, and the birth rate exceeds the death rate, the population under favorable conditions must grow exponentially.

where *M* is a "threshold" factor. If population density falls below this, survival of the population is impossible and sooner or later it passes to extinction. The determination of *M* is obviously of vital importance in the conservation efforts now being made to preserve numerous endangered species.

The simple models of population growth so far described are all *deterministic*, that is, for a given set of conditions they provide only *one* set of answers. This would approximate fairly well to real world situations if the populations modeled were always very large. Indeed, still further refinements of deterministic models have been developed which simulate oscillation about particular density values, as described earlier. However, in the smaller populations usually under examination, biological variation normally intervenes to offer a number of possible outcomes. Thus, for example, neither laboratory nor field populations, when observed over long periods, are found actually to hold steady on an asymptote. It is therefore more accurate to simulate population growth by using *stochastic* models, which take probabilities into account. The additional mathematical involvement can be handled by the use of computers. A discussion of such recent developments may be found in Krebs (1972). Nevertheless, despite such reservations concerning the applicability of deterministic as contrasted with stochastic models of population growth, the quantitative effects of environmental factors on this process, as described in the next chapter, have generally been made on a deterministic basis.

Optimum Yield

Stable populations are of intrinsic theoretical interest but in terms of the bioenergetics of consumer trophic levels in ecosystems are of little concern. They cannot be exploited without causing some decline. As seen also from the logistic curve of population growth, any removal of individuals by a predator once stability has been achieved must result in a population decline. The least effect of predation will be felt at the point where the logistic curve is steepest. This will also be the point at which the maximum yield can be obtained. It is one half of K, sometimes expressed as $K/2$.

The demographic concepts of factors that determine population size introduced so far have to be supplemented by two further considerations. These are *population age composition* and individual *survivorship* within the population. These further features are now examined in this order in terms of *population structure.*

Population Structure

The most important demographic feature of any member of a population is whether or not it is currently reproducing. For this reason, populations are commonly divided into *preproductive, reproductive,* and *postreproductive* sections. Also, this division is usually superimposed upon an age-class separation (Figure 1-10).

Age Pyramids

As shown in Figure 1-10, when age-class pyramids are constructed, they may fall into one of three basic types. If the mortality that occurs in each successive age class is just sufficient to provide for the maturation to that

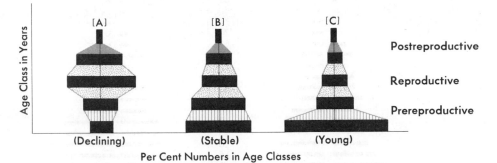

Per Cent Numbers in Age Classes

Figure 1-10. Age pyramids. Theoretical pyramids representing a low, a medium, and a high percentage of young individuals in the population. Age classes can be grouped as here into the immature (prereproductive), fecund (reproductive), and nonfecund (postreproductive) sections.

age class of the same number of individuals, the population distribution will remain the same and the population size will be stable. In a *young* type of population structure, far more individuals are surviving from each age class than are needed for replacement. This is a growth situation with respect to the total number of individuals. Contrariwise, if too few individuals are maturing to provide replacement, the structure will be that of a *declining* population.

In human populations it is customary to display the age structure of the population in five-year age classes. It is also conventional to divide the pyramid so that males are shown on the left and females on the right. One of the classical diagrams comparing the age structures of different human populations is illustrated in Figure 1-11. This figure contrasts a declining population resulting from continuing crofting (small farming) operations and the stable population structure maintained following industrialization. In this instance, as in those previously discussed, it is assumed that migration is at such a low level as to have no significant effect on population structure.

Survivorship

Population structure is thus of critical interest in demography because it affects both the gross fertility rate and the gross mortality rate for a total population. The fertility rate can be determined by observation, as can the mortality rate, the theoretical minimum value being zero. Although mortality can be expressed in a number of ways, it is generally expressed as *specific mortality,* that is, the number of members of an original population dying after the lapse of a given time in a given age group. Human demographers use *age-specific mortality rate,* the number of deaths in a year of females in each five-year age class, divided by the mid-year population of females in that age class. (Likewise, *age-specific fertility* is the number

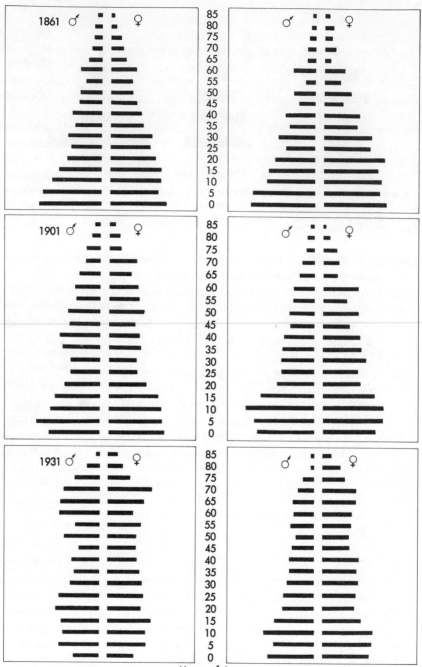

Figure 1-11. Age pyramids for man from two localities. The series on the left is for a declining population, that on the right for a more stable population. Both localities are in Scotland, and the pyramids are constructed from figures obtained between 1861 and 1931. The males are on the left and the females on the right of the pyramids. After F. F. Darling, *American Scientist,* 39:244–256 (1951).

of births of *female* infants per year in each five-year class, divided by the mid-year female population of that age class.)

As mortality varies positively with age in the majority of organisms, the specific mortalities at particular ages can be illustrated in the form of a *life table*. In those circumstances in which age at the death of an animal can be determined from its remains—for example, from the dentition or the horns—a life table, such as on the one in Table 1-1, can be constructed. This table lists the age at death of mountain sheep in Mount McKinley National Park, in Dall, Alaska. The records were obtained by an estimation of the age of mortality from the sheep horns, which persist for many years after the death of the animals. From the table it appears that the average age at death of these mountain sheep is a little more than seven years. Moreover, if a sheep can survive into its second year of life, despite the abundance of wolf predators and the challenges of the environment, it has a better than fair chance of attaining what for this kind of animal is old age. In human societies, actuaries use life tables to calculate the cost of insurance for an individual in any particular age group.

Because what is really vital for the population is not which members die, but which members survive, specific mortality can also be expressed by a *survivorship curve* (Figure 1-12). If it could be assumed that all

Table 1-1. Life Table for Mountain Sheep in Dall, Alaska

Age (years)	Age as Per Cent Deviation from Mean Length of Life	Number Dying in Age Interval per 1,000 Born	Number Surviving at Beginning of Age Interval per 1,000 Born	Mortality Rate per 1,000 Alive at Beginning of Age Interval	Expectation of Life, or Mean Lifetime Remaining to Those Attaining Age Interval (years)
0–0.5	−100.0	54	1,000	54.0	7.06
0.5–1	−93.0	145	946	153.0	—
1–2	−85.9	12	801	15.0	7.7
2–3	−71.8	13	789	16.5	6.8
3–4	−57.7	12	776	15.5	5.9
4–5	−43.5	30	764	39.3	5.0
5–6	−29.5	46	734	62.6	4.2
6–7	−15.4	48	688	69.9	3.4
7–8	−1.1	69	640	108.0	2.6
8–9	+13.0	132	571	231.0	1.9
9–10	+27.0	187	439	426.0	1.3
10–11	+41.0	156	252	619.0	0.9
11–12	+55.0	90	96	937.0	0.6
12–13	+69.0	3	6	500.0	1.2
13–14	+84.0	3	3	1,000.0	0.7

After E. S. Deevey, *The Quarterly Review of Biology*, 22:283–314 (1947).

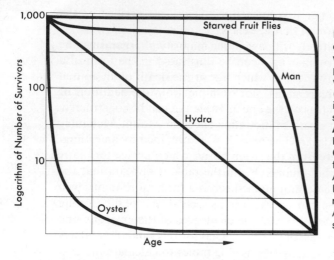

Figure 1-12. Survivorship curves for four organisms with contrasting mortality phases, on the basis of survivors per 1,000 log scale (vertical coordinate) and age in relative units of mean life span (horizontal coordinate). **A**: Oyster, from egg stage. **B**: Hydra, from blastocyst stage. **C**: Man, from birth. **D**: Starved fruit flies, from emergence. After E. S. Deevey, "The Probability of Death." Copyright © 1950 by Scientific American, Inc. All rights reserved.

members of an original population had the same capacity for survival (environmental effects for the moment are ignored), plotting the number of surviving individuals against time would produce a survivorship curve in the form of a right angle. Some populations in culture do approximate this theoretical postulate.

Starved fruit flies die after almost the same interval of time. When a survivorship curve is constructed by the plotting of the number of survivors against time, the resulting curve for a starved fruit fly population, composed of individuals raised from similarly aged batches of eggs, is extremely convex with a sharp angle. With the lowered infantile mortality rate that modern medicine has made possible, the survivorship curve for a contemporary human society such as that of the United States approximates that of the starved fruit fly population. By contrast, in many invertebrate and plant populations there is an extremely high embryonic and juvenile mortality, producing a concave survivorship curve. In a number of bird populations, once the fledgling stage is passed, mortality may occur at an equal rate at any phase of development—a straight-line survivorship relationship. Each of these survival patterns is illustrated in Figure 1-12.

This theoretical consideration of survivorship rates, as expressing the rate of mortality, is based on an original population of the same age. In actuality, because at each interval of time new members are being born, old and other ones dying, both natality and mortality have to be expressed on an age-specific basis, as, it has already been noted, is done in human demography. Given the life table for a population, which expresses the age-structure, and age-specification natality and mortality rates, it is possible to project far more accurate figures for population increase than are obtained from the value obtained from Equation 1-5. However these age-specific methods still have the same limitations as guesses about future mortality and fertility rates.

Such accurate figures are of considerable theoretical application to other than the purely demographic aspects of population ecology, as will be discussed more fully in later chapters. It has, for example, already been noted that in terms of *yield* a population whose density is at $K/2$ is the most productive. For a predator it is obviously not sufficient that it attack the prey population at this stage. There will be still further advantage in avoiding the reproductive age groups and predating the pre- and post-reproductive ones, especially the latter, which is what a trophy hunter may do. Lions preying on wildebeests take especially the young yearlings. Man preying on sea birds usually takes the eggs.

Quite the opposite applies to colonization. A rapid rate of population growth and early establishment of a species in a new habitat are best achieved if the colonizing individuals are in the reproductive age group. In the same way, selection of particular individuals as more "fit" at this reproductive phase will have the greatest impact on the genetic composition of a species.

With the exception of declining populations, which must become extinct, whatever its structure a population will eventually stabilize. It will do so, however, only if the environment remains constant. For a young population this is not possible under natural conditions. The impact of a rapidly increasing population density so modifies the environment as usually to trigger various density-dependent mechanisms.

Seasonal Fluctuations in Population Density

So far, fluctuations in population size have been considered without any reference to periodicity, ignoring the possibility of seasonal variation.

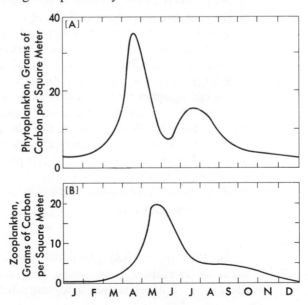

Figure 1-13. Seasonal fluctuations in plankton. A: Phytoplankton. **B:** Zooplankton. After H. B. Moore, *Marine Ecology* (New York: John Wiley & Sons, Inc., 1965).

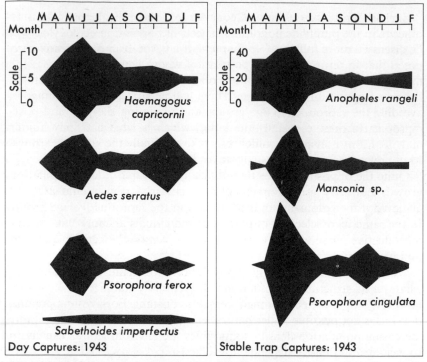

Figure 1-14. Seasonal changes in the abundance of seven species of mosquitoes in the tropical environment of eastern Colombia. All but one species show a marked seasonal variation in population density. After M. Bates, *Journal of Animal Ecology,* 14:17–25 (1945).

1-14

Actually this is so frequent an occurrence that it is a familiar experience of everyday life. At particular times of the year houseflies or mosquitoes are a nuisance, the pollen count is up and reported on radio and television, or butterflies abound. An example of a less popularly observed periodicity is the seasonal fluctuation in the population density of phytoplankton in both fresh-water and marine situations (Figure 1-13).

Marked seasonal fluctuations in population density are encountered as frequently in tropical and arctic regions as they are in temperate regions. Thus M. Bates, investigating the population densities of mosquitoes in Colombia, found that only one species failed to show marked seasonal fluctuation (Figure 1-14). In tropical areas these seasonal fluctuations tend to be correlated with variations in the seasonal incidence of rainfall, whereas in temperate and arctic areas they are correlated with the prevailing temperatures.

Cycles

The least understood population-density variations are those that occur at intervals of some years. The most familiar record of one of these is the biblical reference to seven lean years and seven fat ones, when Pharaoh in a dream saw seven fat cows and seven lean ones. Rainfall in the middle sections of the Nile Valley has been found in modern times to fluctuate on a seven-year cycle. Because the area cultivated in any one year in Egypt depended at one time on the extent of the land flooded by the Nile, which related to the amount of rain falling in its middle and upper reaches, this cycle may well have accounted for the biblical occurrence of famine years.

Cyclic fluctuations in population density of mammals, birds, insects, and fishes and in seed production have been noted, mostly on a three-to-four-year cycle, as in the case of the migration of lemmings, or a nine-to-ten-year cycle, as reported for snowshoe hares. Fluctuations in sunspot activity were at one time believed to be correlated with the longer-term cycles, as the average activity cycle is about eleven years. However, no correlation with sunspot activity or with any other environmental phenomenon has yet been unequivocally established, and cyclic fluctuations are now generally believed to be of a random nature.

Circadian Rhythms

Cyclic behavior of a much shorter periodicity fluctuating over a twenty-four-hour interval—has been widely demonstrated. The rate of metabolism of mammals is controlled by a *biological clock* that imposes what is called a circadian rhythm on such physiological activities as sleep, excretion, maintenance of body temperature, and perspiration. The term *circadian* comes from the periodicity of such cycles, which approximates one day. In these times of very rapid air transit, these rhythms can be readily disturbed in man by a few hours' flight to east or west. A feeling of tiredness and unease in the new situation is the usual experience for several days, until the circadian rhythm can be reset. Astronauts making rapid revolutions of the earth inevitably return tired if not exhausted from long stays in space, where they are unable to adjust their circadian rhythms to a far shorter day and night.

The behavior of many animals and plants follows a diurnal-nocturnal pattern. The times of feeding and drinking, of singing and calling, of flower opening and leaf movement, and of anthesis and spore relase may all recur on a twenty-four-hour cycle.

Although the principal environmental factors that vary over a twenty-four-hour period include light, temperature, and humidity, it seems probable that in the largest number of instances the circadian behavior is a response to light. Andrewartha and Birch cite many animal species whose diurnal activity is so controlled. These include cockroaches, crickets, beetles, deer mice, field mice, crabs, and fruit flies. In all such instances more than a direct response to the light stimulus is involved, for the circadian rhythm of activity will continue, for a time at least, in both total darkness and continuous light. There is less evidence for circadian responses to diurnal fluctuations in temperature and humidity, factors that in any case may be difficult to separate, as was seen earlier. Some work on fruit flies does suggest that their rhythms are selected to avoid activity in the middle of the day, when they might be exposed to dessication.

That circadian rhythms, and also to a lesser extent the longer yearly or circannual ones, are imposed by some form of biological-clock mechanism within the organism itself is indicated by the continuation of the circadian activity when the external stimulus is removed. The general independence of circadian rhythms from temperature responses further evidences the existence of an internal rhythm independent, for a time, at least, of external stimuli.

Social Distance

Of interest to hunters are two little-investigated developments of social or individual distance, *flight distance* and *charge distance*—the distances at which animals are liable to flee and charge, respectively. Animals with good sight, such as the sable antelope, detect potential danger at a considerable distance and have a great flight distance. By temperament the sable antelope is not aggressive, so that its charge distance is only several meters. Hence, the animal is not dangerous unless it has been wounded. The rhinoceros, on the other hand, can see very poorly and its flight distance is not great. By temperament the rhinoceros is aggressive, so that its charge distance is considerable—several dozen meters. Hence, it is a dangerous animal to hunt. The elephant, likewise, has poor eyesight and a restricted flight distance, but because it has a more complacent temperament than the rhinoceros, its charge distance is appreciably shorter. Because of this, contemporary hunters have been able to get so close to elephants that they have been able to kill them with a bow and arrow. Some older zoological gardens may still confine animals in enclosures that have a lesser radius than their flight distance. It would be surmised that such enclosures would have to be seriously disturbing to the wild animals concerned.

Spacing is one other aspect of the distance between individuals that must be described, as it may be considered an ethological regulatory mechanism. There are three possible ways in which individuals in a population may be dispersed, that is, spaced relative to one another; spacing may be *uniform, random,* or *clumped* (Figure 1-15). Invertebrates, for example, form populations containing uniformly spaced individuals.

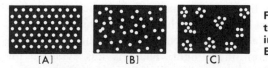

[A]   [B]   [C]

Figure 1-15. Three basic patterns of spacing of individuals in a population. A: Uniform. B: Random. C: Clumped.

Random spacing is also not unusual, occurring particularly among plants with dispersal mechanisms that saturate the air with seeds. However, some form of close aggregation of groups of individuals, or clumping, is by far the most common occurrence. Even mating pairs and their newborn offspring may be regarded as clumped; they are paralleled in plants by the distribution of propagules in the vicinity of the parent. Besides such clumping for reproductive reasons, animals aggregate in swarms, herds, flocks, or colonies for greater facility of feeding and sometimes in order to increase the chances of avoiding predation. In accordance with what is commonly known as *Allee's principle,* each species has an optimum clumping value; overcrowding beyond this density or undercrowding below it will tend to act as a limiting factor in population regulation. These and other aspects of social distance are considered further in Chapter 5.

References and Further Readings

Chitty, D. H. "The Natural Selection of Self-Regulatory Behavior in Animal Populations." *Proceedings of the Ecological Society of Australia,* 2:51–78 (1967).

Frank, P. V. "Prediction of Population Growth Form in *Daphnia pulex* Cultures." *The American Naturalist,* 94:357–372 (1960).

Krebs, C. J. "The Lemming Cycle at Barker Lake, Northwest Territories During 1959–62 Discussion." *Arctic Institute of North America Technical Paper,* No. 15, 50–57 (1964).

————. "Population Growth." In *Ecology,* C. J. Krebs. New York: Harper & Row, Publishers, 1972, pp. 182–210.

Leslie, P. H. "The Intrinsic Rate of Increase and the Overlap of Successive Generations in a Population of Guillemots (*Uria aalge* Pont)." *Journal of Animal Ecology,* 35:291–301 (1966).

Lloyd, M., and H. S. Dybas. "The Periodical Cicada Problem. II." *Evolution,* 20:466–505 (1966).

Murdoch, W. W. "Population Stability and Life History Phenomena." *American Naturalist,* 100:5–11 (1966).

Orians, G. H. "Natural Selection and Ecological Theory." *American Naturalist,* 96:257–263 (1962).

Pielou, E. C. "A Single Mechanism to Account for Regular, Random and Aggregated Populations." *Journal of Ecology,* 48:575–584 (1960).

Richards, O. W. "The Theoretical and Practical Study of Natural Insect Populations." *Annual Review of Entomology,* 6:147–162 (1961).

Slobodkin, L. B. *Growth and Regulation of Animal Populations.* New York: Holt, Rinehart and Winston, Inc., 1961.

Smith, F. E. "Population Dynamics in *Daphnia magna* and a New Model for Population Growth." *Ecology,* 44:651–663 (1963).

Solomon, M. E. *Population Dynamics.* New York: St. Martin's Press, Inc., 1969.

Southward, T. B. E. "The Interpretation of Population Change." *Journal of Animal Ecology,* 36:519–529 (1967).

Utida, S. "Cyclic Fluctuations of Population Density Intrinsic to the Host-Parasite System." *Ecology,* 38:442–449 (1957).

UTIDA, S. "Population Fluctuation, and Experimental and Theoretical Approach." *Cold Spring Harbor Symposium on Quantitative Biology,* 22:139–151 (1957).

WATSON, A. (ed.) "Animal Populations in Relation to Their Food Resources." *British Ecological Society Symposium,* No. 10. Oxford: Blackwell Scientific Publications Ltd., 1970.

WATSON, A., and D. JENKINS. "Experiments on Population Control by Territorial Behavior in Red Grouse." *Journal of Animal Ecology,* 37:595–614 (1968).

WILSON, E. O., and W. H. BOSSERT. *A Primer of Population Biology.* Stamford, Conn.: Sinauer Associates, Inc., 1972.

WYNNE-EDWARDS, V. C. "Population Control in Animals." *Scientific American,* 211(6):68–74 (1964).

———. "Regulation in Animal Societies and Population." In *Regulation and Control in Living Systems,* H. Kalmus (ed.) New York: John Wiley & Sons, Inc., 1966, pp. 397–421.

Chapter 2 • The Environmental Relationships of Populations

Populations cannot exist, any more or less than other living systems, without involvement in some form of interaction with their physical and chemical environment. An examination of the nature of this environmental interaction was one of the earliest tasks undertaken by population ecologists. Such studies in physiological ecology still represent a considerable proportion of the total ecological effort. However, partly for the reasons already mentioned in the Preface, that is, the various recent improvements in instrumentation and the added sophistication that they provide, these environmental studies are increasingly more field than laboratory oriented. This is all the more so because it has been realized that a plurality of environmental factors tends to have a synergistic rather than a simple additive effect. This is especially the case with respect to what at one time were known as *limiting factors*.

Essential Elements and Limiting Factors

Individual organisms of a population in order to grow and reproduce must be supplied with certain essential substances. Of the ninety-two naturally occurring chemical elements on our planet, organisms utilize approximately one third. These include carbon, hydrogen, oxygen, nitrogen, sulfur, calcium, phosphorus, potassium, sodium, silica, magnesium, boron, manganese, iron, zinc, molybdenum, copper, iodine, and cobalt. The amounts of these elements that particular organisms require vary enormously. Carbon, oxygen, and hydrogen are found in the molecules of all living systems. Cobalt and copper, on the other hand, are less extensively utilized in cells and are needed in much lower quantity. The last nine elements listed are among those usually known as *trace elements*, because of the minute quantities of them necessary for the growth of organisms. In practice, chemical elements are now considered by ecologists not so much by virtue of their effects on individual populations, although these are still important, but rather in terms of the individual circulation patterns in which they are cycled through ecosystems. In this context, those elements used most commonly by producers are conveniently categorized into *gaseous elements,* like hydrogen, oxygen, nitrogen, and chlorine; *macronutrients,* like carbon, potassium, calcium, magnesium, phosphorus, and sulfur; *micronutrients* (trace elements), like manganese, copper, zinc, iron, boron, and molybdenum; and *nonessential elements,* like sodium, aluminum, barium, strontium, rubidium, lead, and others.

The Liebig-Blackman Law

The relationship between the available amounts of essential elements and plant growth was first investigated by Baron Justus von Liebig in 1840. He discovered that crop yield was frequently limited by elements other than those such as the macronutrients listed in the last paragraph, which were utilized in the largest quantities. Paraphrasing a part of his statement he concluded from his experimental results that "growth is dependent on the amount of food stuff that is present in minimum quantity." This statement has come to be known as Liebig's law of the minimum (Figure 2-1 **A**). It is now generally combined with a law of limiting factors first propounded by F. F. Blackman. This British physiologist early in this century investigated the factors affecting the rate of photosynthesis. He discovered that the rate is governed by the level of the one factor that is operating at a limiting intensity (Figure 2-1 **B**).

Subsequent work on limiting factors and substances has shown that these original concepts are too simplistic. Although in theory the concepts are still valid, limiting factors and substances more usually operate within an ecological system in combination rather than alone. A high level of one factor or substance will modify the limiting effect of another, a process known as *factor interaction.* For example, in standard agronomic fertilizer trials, it is common to carry out experiments on the effect of added nitrogen, potassium, and phosphorus salts on yields. The plot design in such experiments permits each element to be tested separately, and in combination with one or both of the others. Because of factor interaction, the results of such NPK manurial trials must always be examined by multivariate analysis, a statistical procedure that determines the nature of the individual effect of these three substances when acting alone and when interacting with one or both of the others.

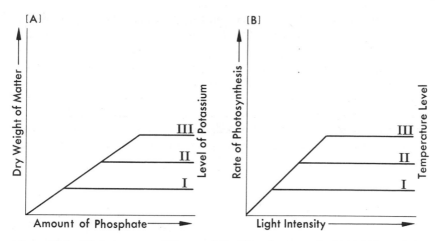

Figure 2-1. Minimum quantities and limiting factors. A: Liebig's law of the minimum. The amount of phosphate (horizontal coordinate) plotted against the dry weight of matter produced (vertical coordinate) at three different levels of the supply of potassium, which eventually becomes limiting at each level. **B:** Blackman's law of limiting factors. The rate of photosynthesis (vertical coordinate) plotted against the light intensity (horizontal coordinate) at three different temperatures, each of which eventually limits the rate of photosynthesis.

For a population established in an environment that is not too extreme for any single limiting factor, its growth and reproduction are normally determined by the interaction of all factors rather than by the sole influence of the one that happens to be limiting at a given moment of time. The analysis of factor interaction under natural conditions is therefore extremely complex. Despite the now general availability of electronic data processing for the computational work involved in such an analysis, physiological ecologists still prefer, if at all possible, to observe or manipulate one factor at a time in order to determine its effect when it becomes limiting. Numerous modifications of the Liebig-Blackman law have been suggested, and a time factor has been added. Many ecologists, however, believe that this law is best retained in its simpler forms.

Shelford's Law

The dispersal and growth of populations is determined not only by too *little* of an element or too *low* an intensity of a particular ecological factor, it may also be restricted by too *much* of the element or too *high* an intensity of the factor. For example, carbon dioxide is necessary for the growth of all living plants; small increases in the amount of concentration of carbon dioxide in the atmosphere will increase the rate of plant growth. Very considerable increases become toxic. Likewise, small additions of arsenic to the human diet actually have a tonic effect; increases in the dosage, however, soon prove fatal.

The idea that factors could be limiting at their maximum as well as their minimum levels was incorporated in a law of tolerance presented by V. E. Shelford in 1913. This law postulates that each ecological factor to which an organism responds has maximum and minimum limiting effects between which lies a range that is now known as the *limits of tolerance*. Many studies in physiological ecology, especially in plants, have been concerned with the tolerance limits of various populations. These have added considerably to our knowledge concerning population dispersal patterns and to our understanding of the variation within species populations.

Limiting and Tolerance Concepts Combined

A more complete expression of the ecological conditions determining the dispersal and growth of populations is obtained in a combination of the Liebig-Blackman idea of the minimum with Shelford's theory of limits of tolerance. It can then be postulated that the establishment of a particular population in a given area is dependent upon the availability of the necessary substances in the required minimum quantity and the functioning of critical physical factors at the required minimal level, combined with the occurrence of these elements and the operation of these factors within the tolerance limits of the members of the populations.

The application of these combined concepts to ecology provides an approach that enables the physiological ecologist to begin to penetrate the complex environmental relationships of a natural ecosystem. It is usually possible to detect at least one element or factor in the physical environment that is likely to be limiting and to proceed to observe what occurs when this element or factor varies or is manipulated. Among aquatic populations, for example, it is unlikely that water will be a limiting factor. By contrast, investigation of the effect of water as a limiting factor in a desert habitat would be an obvious starting point for any ecological study. In the same way, in a terrestrial environment there would seem to be little point in commencing a project with the determination of the oxygen content of the air at different heights, for this is to all intents and purposes hardly variable under natural conditions. By contrast, in an aquatic environment the oxygen content of the water at various depths probably has great significance in regard to the dispersal of particular populations, and exploration of this relationship would be expected to prove a valuable initial exercise.

Energy Exchange and the Environment

In all interactions between populations and their environments there is an exchange of energy. Indeed, this is what such interactions represent. Ecologists have consciously or unconsciously come to isolate one form of energy exchange from all others, perhaps because its values are several magnitudes higher than all others and have thus set it apart. This is the energy exchange that proceeds at a rate high enough for a population to procure sufficient input from it to power its life processes, whether in the form of radiant energy for autotrophs or chemical energy for heterotrophs. This special form of energy exchange is explored by community ecologists and is considered in Chapter 6 of this text. It is usually conventionally excluded from the investigations of environmental ecologists, just as it is separately treated here. Likewise, population interactions are separated from physical and chemical features of the environment. Thus, for pedagogical purposes the treatment of environment in this chapter refers mainly to such physical parameters as temperature, wind and precipitation, and chemical features like the availability of particular inorganic nutrients, water, or oxygen. Although of a different order of magnitude, it must always be remembered that such environmental interactions are no more and no less than an interchange of energy.

Environmental ecologists sometimes regard the environment as an independent ecological entity, having an existence distinct from the populations that interact with it. To do so is perhaps as unrealistic as to consider, for example, particle physics independently of the observer and his various sensors. Moreover, some plant-oriented environmentalists argue that to make a distinction between physical or *abiotic,* and biological or *biotic* environmental factors is somewhat arbitrary. Animal-orientalists have a lesser tendency to do so, for the effects of biotic interactions deriving from animal populations are generally more dramatic. A predator literally *devours* its prey; few abiotic factors to which a population is normally exposed are quite so immediately or so completely terminal in their effects. However, whatever philosophy is adopted, there always have to be two-way interactions between populations and their environment. These obviously vary in both space and time and the task of environmental ecologists is to identify and trace such patterns and their abiotic and biotic interactions.

Climatic Factors

Of all the abiotic environmental factors affecting terrestrial populations, climatic factors have been the most investigated. Many attempts have been made to express climate in a quantitative manner in order to obtain a correlation between climate as a limiting factor and the occurrence of particular populations. These attempts have usually taken the form of numerical expressions of moisture and temperature, modified by their effectiveness. One of the best known of these, that of C. W. Thornthwaite, provides a comparison of precipitation and potential evapotranspiration (the temperature-dependent loss of water from the surface soil and plants by evaporation).

Thornthwaite expresses climate in the form of a precipitation-effectiveness index. This is based on the annual mean of the precipitation-evaporation ratios (P/E) recorded through the year. One obtains the index by dividing P, the mean precipitation, by E, the mean monthly amount of evaporation from the water surface of a meteorological pan. Thornthwaite then devised a monthly coefficient of temperature efficiency in the following manner:

$$T\text{-}E \text{ index} = \sum_{n=1}^{12} \left(\frac{T - 32}{4}\right)_n$$

where T = mean monthly temperature for a station.

A range of precipitation-effectiveness indices, with the climates and vegetation types to which they generally apply, is shown in Table 2-1.

Thornthwaite's figures provide a fairly good fit with the distribution of vegetation in North America as shown in Figure 2-2, which contrasts the climates of three different ecological regions of the continent and illustrates the varying occurrence of maximum water utilization. In the deciduous forest of the northeastern United States, water is only limiting toward the end of the dry summer; occasional summer droughts do not disturb the forest, which can tolerate some water strain, but can have a disastrous effect on the yield of *annual* crops. In the winter-rainfall area of the Pacific Coast, growth and reproduction occur mostly in late winter and early spring. Annual crops that grow in the winter and perennial ones, such as oranges, need irrigation in the summer, but the natural fauna and flora can survive this rainless period. In the desert, the vegetation shows various adaptations that enable it to survive long drought periods, and the animals possess mechanisms that restrict or entirely avoid dependence on free water for drinking; no crops can be grown without irrigation.

Looking at the *global* picture of climate, the same sorts of correlated patterns are observable as those that can be identified in North America. Global climatic patterns are determined by dynamic weather systems.

Table 2-1. Thornthwaite's *P/E* ratio. A selection of values for the Thornthwaite precipitation-effectiveness index is shown here with the climatic and vegetation type with which they usually correspond. Within certain limits, the amount of standing crop is positively correlated with the *P/E* index of a region.

Type of Climate	Type of Vegetation	*P/E* Index
Wet	Rain forest	> 128
Humid	Forest	64—127
Subhumid	Grassland	32—63
Semiarid	Steppe	16—31
Arid	Desert	< 16

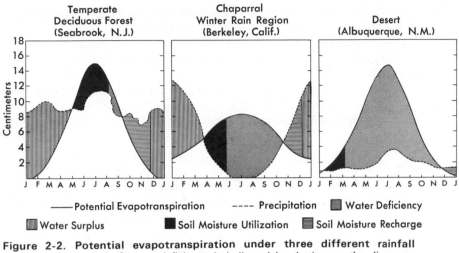

Figure 2-2. Potential evapotranspiration under three different rainfall regimes. The period of water deficiency is indicated by dotting on the diagrams; this is the period when water can become a limiting factor to growth. After C. W. Thornthwaite, *Journal of Marine Research,* 14:510–515 (1955).

Heated by solar energy, cooled by radiation, these systems comprise air masses constantly in motion. This movement results from temperature and pressure differences and is modified by interaction with forces arising from the rotation of the Earth and friction between these moving air masses and the Earth's surface. In the Northern Hemisphere, the main movement from the pole to about 30°N is eastward, the prevailing winds being westerlies. South of the equator, in this equivalent latitudinal zone, it is the same. About 30°N and S are the "horse latitudes," where winds are relatively slight. The sinking air masses in these regions can deposit no rain and deserts result, as in the Sahara and Arabia north of the equator, Chile and southern Africa in the Southern Hemisphere. The equatorial belt between the 20° latitudes has prevailing rain-bearing trade winds, northeasterlies to the north, southeasterlies to the south.

This general atmospheric circulation pattern of air masses is little disturbed over the great oceans but becomes quite complicated over the continental land masses. Despite enormous and worldwide efforts on the part of meteorologists to evolve predictive computer models, we still *record* climate rather than forecasting it.

The boundary between different air masses forms a *front.* There are many kinds of fronts, such as warm, cold, and stationary. It is the frontal systems that bring the weather that determines the climate of a particular region. In North America a very simplistic picture of the climate may be obtained if one views the continent as having three frontal systems. These are a Pacific system with fronts moving in from the west, an Atlantic system with fronts moving in from the east, and a Canadian system with fronts driving down from the north between the two other systems. This pattern of frontal systems can be seen any night on the TV weather news. The summer boundary of the Canadian frontal system coincides with the northern extent of taiga—or boreal forest—its winter boundary with the southern limit in the United States of the spruce-fir populations of this ecosystem.

Climate is therefore a combination of numerous different environmental factors. The various effects of the more significant of these individual environmental components will now be considered.

Temperature

Although specific climatic effects on factors such as populations are frequently attributable to *combinations* of temperature and moisture, it is sometimes possible to identify a temperature factor in operation essentially by itself. This is especially so when ambient temperature approaches the tolerance limits for a particular population.

The temperature tolerance limits of living organisms as a whole are surprisingly narrow by comparison with the temperature range of approximately 150°C in the land, air, and water around us. The upper limit of tolerance becomes critical more rapidly than the lower, the lethal point lying in the region of 55°C, although some lower organisms have adapted to temperatures up to 85°C in hot springs such as those found in in the geyser beds of Yellowstone National Park. The highest temperature encountered in seawater is about 36°C, but shade temperature on land (that is, temperature as recorded by an instrument that is placed about 1.5 m above the ground surface and that does not directly receive radiant energy) can be much higher. A daily maximum of 46°C may be reached for as long as a month in some desert areas. Maximum shade temperatures as high as 55°C have occasionally been reported. This is approaching the thermal death point for protoplasm in many organisms and could poach us like eggs. The lower tolerance limit for temperature is much less critical for life, and very low temperatures may be tolerated for short intervals of time, especially by organisms in a dormant condition. A record air-temperature low of − 70°C is claimed for Siberia, but fresh water cannot fall below 0°C, and seawater below − 2.5°C, without freezing.

Whereas the range of temperature in the sea thus falls within the tolerance limits of the great majority of organisms, air temperatures may be far above and far below these limits. An extension of the temperature tolerance limits has been achieved by birds and mammals (and reportedly certain other animals), which maintain a constant body temperature independently of the environment. Such animals are described as *homothermous* (physiologically temperature-regulated) or, somewhat loosely, warm-blooded. Animals not possessing this precise physiological thermoregulation and all plants are described as *poikilothermous* or cold-blooded. Although poikilothermous animals tend to assume a temperature close to that of the environment and to fluctuate in temperature with the environment, many actually possess behavioral mechanisms permitting a limited regulation of body temperature.

A few relatively simple groups of invertebrates, such as rotifers and nematodes, are able to pass into a resting stage by the almost complete removal of water from the body tissues. In this state of suspended animation, known as *cryptobiosis,* they may survive for over a hundred years. In this condition they can remain viable despite exposure for a number of minutes to temperature exceeding 150°C, or for several days to temperatures approaching absolute zero. Some spores or cysts of micro-organisms, plants, and invertebrates show similar temperate tolerance, but it is more usual to find the integrity of living systems destroyed by such extremes in temperature.

The *duration* of short-term variations in temperature is of considerable ecological importance. A steady figure of, say, 20°C over a twenty-four-hour period may have effects on populations very different from the effects of 30°C by day and 10°C by night. Many organisms appear to be adapted to fluctuating daily temperatures and respond differently if these are averaged out to a steady mean under experimental conditions. This does not apply to marine organisms, for the temperature of substantial bodies of water rarely fluctuates more than 1°C on a daily or other short-term basis.

The extent of short-term variations in temperature is also important if the temperature even briefly exceeds the tolerance limits for particular organisms. The majority of plants and animals have no special mechanism enabling them to survive extremes of temperature such as those described for cryptobionts (Table 2-2). The occurrence of temperatures beyond the tolerance range is commonly the limiting factor in the distribution of particular populations and is also responsible for the selection of subgroups within them.

Table 2-2. Temperature Relations of the Housefly (Musca domestica), including Tolerance Limits (in degrees centigrade)

Death in a few minutes (maximum survival temperature)	46.5
Heat coma	44.6
Excessive activity	40.1
Effective temperature range	
Rapid movement (maximum effective temperature)	27.9
Normal activity	23–15
Feeble movement (minimum effective temperature)	10.8
Stops moving	6.7
Chill coma	6.0
Death in forty minutes (minimum survival temperature)	−5.0

Modified from G. L. Clarke, *Elements of Ecology* (New York: John Wiley & Sons, Inc., 1954), p. 144.

Seasonal variation in temperature of greater amplitude than these daily and other short-term fluctuations is also of considerable ecological significance. It is, for example, the basis for our classification of the year into the four seasons. Although in a maritime climate on the equator this seasonal variation may be as little as 0.5°C, in a continental area in the Middlewest of the United States, such as Minnesota, it rises to about 35°C. A seasonal range of nearly 80°C is reported from Tibet.

Over the Earth's surface, temperatures vary widely, vertically as well as horizontally. Vertical changes of temperature are also of ecological interest. It is allowed that for every 150-meter gain in altitude, there is a decrease in temperature of approximately 1°C. On this basis, a tropical mountain with an air temperature of 33°C at its foot will be estimated to have a snow line at about five thousand meters, as is indeed the case with Mount Chimborazo in Ecuador and Mount Kilimanjaro in Tanganyika, for example. The generally recognized broad climatic zones on the mountains of North America (Figure 2-3) are based essentially on changes in temperature associated with change in altitude. The situation is complex, however; other factors, such as moisture, atmospheric pressure, and insolation, also intervene and interact with the altitudinal temperature changes. Temperature may thus have a determining ecological effect on

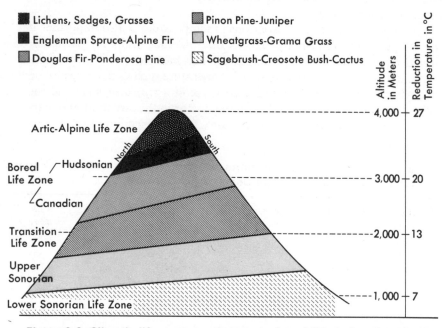

Figure 2-3. Climatic life zones on the mountains of North America, showing the vertical sequence in the central Rocky Mountains. The tilting of the zones between the north and south slopes arises from an interaction between temperature and moisture. The south slopes are drier, and the zonation on the south slopes generally is higher because of the added water stress.

the latitudinal, seasonal, and altitudinal dispersal of populations. Aside from this biotic interaction, there are also certain vital physical effects.

The differential heating of the atmosphere resulting from temperature variation over the Earth's surface produces environmental perturbations, including local and trade winds and hurricanes and other storms; but more importantly it determines the global distribution pattern of precipitation.

Precipitation

When a layer of air saturated with moisture is driven upward by striking a land mass or another moving mass of air, the more rarefied atmosphere into which is ascends allows it to expand, with consequent cooling. If the chilling of the rising air mass passes the condensation point, water droplets or ice crystals will be formed. These may fall to the ground as rain, hail, snow, or sleet—all forms of *precipitation* (Figure 2-4). The windward side of a mountain mass, where air masses are deflected upward, is therefore

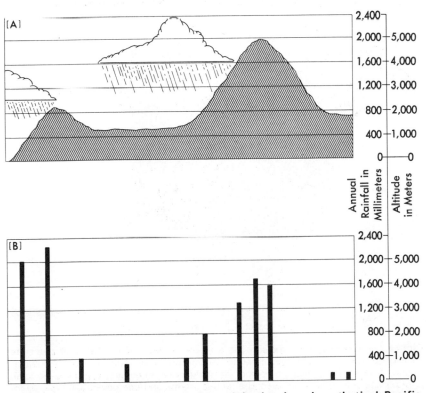

Figure 2-4. Composite diagram of precipitation in a hypothetical Pacific Coast situation, showing the high rainfall near the coastline and at medium elevations and the rain-shadow effect.

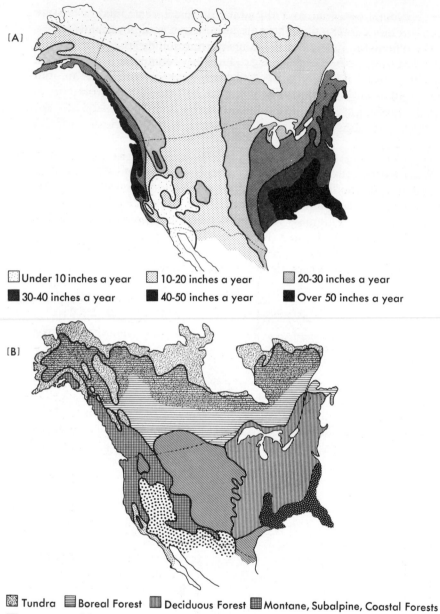

[A]

☐ Under 10 inches a year   ☐ 10-20 inches a year   ☐ 20-30 inches a year
■ 30-40 inches a year   ■ 40-50 inches a year   ■ Over 50 inches a year

[B]

▨ Tundra ▥ Boreal Forest ▥ Deciduous Forest ▦ Montane, Subalpine, Coastal Forests
▨ Grassland ■ Southern Conifer Forest ▥ Desert ▧ Chaparral

Figure 2-5. Correlation between the amount of annual rainfall and the type of vegetation. A: Distribution of annual rainfall zones over North America. **B:** Distribution of the major vegetation types of North America. In some instances, there is an approximate coincidence between one rainfall regime and one vegetation type, as for example between the area receiving fifty to sixty inches annual rainfall and the southern coniferous forest. In other instances, the vegetation type may cover two rainfall areas, as is the case with the boreal-forest and deciduous-forest vegetation.

wetter than the leeward side. The leeward side lies in a rain shadow because the air masses are falling and becoming warmer; they consequently have a lower relative humidity, that is, a higher saturation deficit.

The amount of snowfall and its persistence comprise a major local ecological factor in colder areas. In general, the distribution and amount of rainfall is of great ecological significance. The world distribution of major vegetation types shows a broad correlation with rainfall patterns; similar correlations can be established for the North American continent (Figure 2-5).

Much of the northeastern United States lies in a summer rainfall regime. The Pacific Coast receives somewhat similar quantities of rain but as winter rainfall, the result of special meteorological conditions that are found only in a few other situations about the Earth. This winter rainfall regime, wherever it occurs, is associated with a sclerophyllous type of shrubby vegetation that is known in the United States as *chaparral*, elsewhere as *maquis*.

Evapotranspiration

On a more local basis, the action of rainfall is generally confounded with the operation of other ecological factors. One of these combined effects is expressed in the form of water loss by evaporation from plant and soil surfaces, universally known as *evapotranspiration*.

Many studies have been made of evapotranspiration in crop plants. A summary of this work has been provided by H. L. Penman, a physicist working at the Rothamsted Agricultural Experiment Station in England. Through his investigations, Penman was able to show that evapotranspiration may be regarded as an entirely physical process and expressed in physical parameters. Provided that there is no difference in color, the evapotranspiration from a given area of vegetation will be independent of the nature and biomass of that vegetation and simply a function of the radiant energy received. Thus, a hectare of forest will lose by evapotranspiration no more and no less water than a hectare of grass under comparable conditions. This is not to say that *seasonal* differences will not occur. Over a whole year an evergreen tree cover may lose *more* water than a deciduous one—or a grassland, in which shoots die down during the winter. In some parts of the world, the removal of a natural tree cover for the purpose of cultivating annual crops on the land may so drastically curtail evapotranspiration that the additional water accruing to the water table will cause it to rise so close to the surface as to inhibit crop growth (Figure 2-6).

In one further respect, to consider *total* precipitation or *total* evapotranspiration may be an oversimplification of its influence as an environmental factor. The total amount of precipitation falling in an area never becomes available to its populations. Some is intercepted by plant foliage

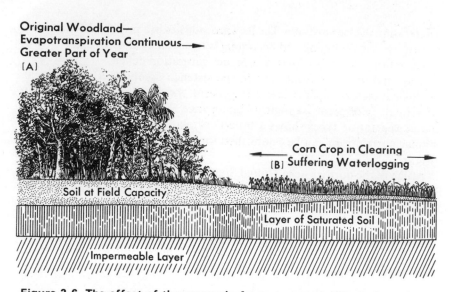

Figure 2-6. The effect of the removal of a tree cover in Rhodesia. In **A**, the level of the water table fluctuates about a mean stable point each year. In **B**, after removal of the tree cover to permit cropping, evapotranspiration losses are reduced and more water penetrates to the water table, which rises close to the surface.

and evaporates again directly. In evergreen forests such as the boreal forest, or the tropical rain forest, light rainfall may, because of this interception, never reach the ground. Even at the soil surface precipitation may not infiltrate. Snow may be blown away and rainfall may flow away as surface runoff. The extent and rate of infiltration will be dependent partly on the nature of the soil, which is considered later in this chapter.

Climographs

Thus, it appears that in most situations two or more major component climatic factors are usually acting in concert. Attempts such as Thornthwaite's to correlate the combined effects of these factors with population behavior are most successful when applied to broad agricultural and forestry zones. For more detailed ecological investigations it is usual to express the combined effects of climatic factors such as precipitation and temperature graphically by plotting one against the other to produce what is known as a *climograph*. Negative coincidence between the tolerance limits for a given population and a particular set of climograph parameters is then likely to be more significant than positive; that is to say, species cannot become established in an area in which climographs indicate that the range of major climatic factors will exceed the tolerance limits of the population (Figure 2-7). The contrary does not necessarily hold true, however. A species may fail in an area in which its tolerance limits do fall

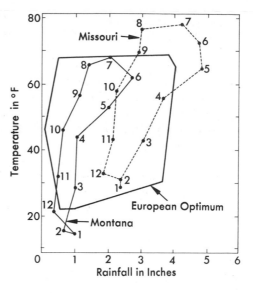

Figure 2-7. Climographs for monthly averages of mean temperature and the amount of rainfall. The dotted line is for Columbia, Mo., and the lighter solid line for Havre, Mont. The solid black line indicates the average temperature-moisture conditions in the European breeding range of the Hungarian partridge, successfully introduced into Montana but failing in Missouri. After A. C. Twoney, *Ecology*, 17:122–132 (1936).

within the climographs for major climatic factors because of the operation of some unconsidered abiotic or biotic environmental feature.

An example of the use of climographs is provided in studies of the relation between climate and vegetation zonation in the northwestern

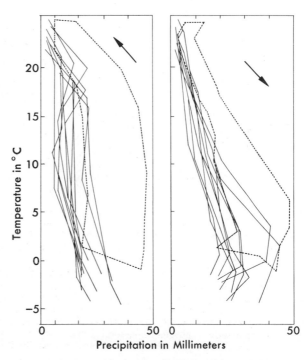

Figure 2-8. Climographs showing the mean monthly temperature and mean median precipitation for a number of weather stations in the sagebrush (*Artemisia*) desert (solid lines), with the pattern of similar data from grassland superimposed (dotted lines). The climograph polygons are separated into halves, with the warming curves shown on the left and the cooling curves on the right. After R. F. Daubenmire, *Ecological Monographs*, 26:131–154 (1956).

United States undertaken by R. F. Daubenmire. He divided the climographs he prepared for this region into two halves—the warming curves of spring and summer and the cooling curves of fall and winter. From the climographs in Figure 2-8 it may be seen how Daubenmire demonstrated the greater extremes of temperature on the desert and the much greater precipitation of the growing season on the grassland in spring.

Such environmental relationships as are expressed in climographs are now commonly depicted in the essentially similar form of a *space diagram.* This is a two-dimensional manner of expressing a three-dimensional relationship. When the parameters of the three dimensions relate to physical features of the environment, such diagrams can be said to represent the *climate space* of a population. The diagram in Figure 2-9 contrasts climate space for a bird and a reptile in terms of radiation, air temperature, and wind speed. This emphasizes a point to be considered further shortly, namely that the ecological effects of temperature may be strongly modified by the amount of air movement, as may those of different air moisture levels.

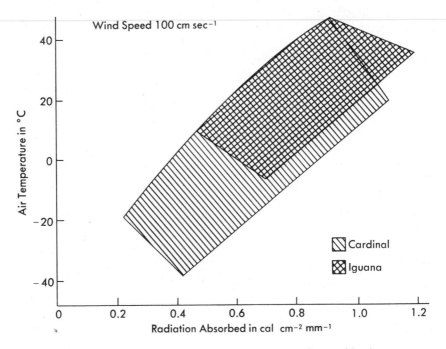

Figure 2-9. A climate space diagram. This contrasts the combined temperature and absorbed radiation limits for a bird (cardinal) and a lizard (desert iguana) when the wind speed is 100 cm-sec^{-1} (2.2 mph). At night (left-hand curve), all animals absorb the same amount of radiation from the same environment. In the daytime (right-hand curve), the larger cardinal has a greater absorptivity, but with increased amounts of absorbed radiation it must seek a lower air temperature. After *Topics in the Study of Life* (New York: Harper & Row, Publishers, 1971).

Of all the environmental factors that influence living systems at the population level the most basic is light. Without this component of solar radiation, the immense number of organisms as we know them could not exist. Light functions as an ecological factor by variations in its intensity, its wavelength, and its duration. In some ways light can be considered as a component of climate, especially when climate refers to total hours of sunlight over a given time period.

Light intensity is of major significance for plants, which have been selected in the situations in which they live for their response to a particular range of light values. When the intensities fall so low that there is insufficient photosynthetic activity to supply the metabolic needs of the plant, the light value is said to have passed the *compensation point*. This low level will normally be approached only near the ground in dense vegetation, where there is considerable light interception by higher layers of plants. Light intensity may also fall below the compensation point on cloudy days, at dawn and dusk, and at depth in aquatic situations. Indeed this value determines the lower limit of the *euphotic zone* in aquatic ecosystems.

Light intensity can be measured and expressed in two ways; in terms of illumination or of energy. The photoelectric cells in light meters record illumination in footcandles. In ecology this form of quantitative expression is now mostly replaced by the gram calorie per square centimeter, correctly but not too familiarly known as a *langley*. Solar radiation arriving at this planet has an intensity of 2 gcal per cm^2. Absorption by the atmosphere, cloud cover, and water vapor reduces this to about 1.3 gcal per cm^2. Of this about 45 per cent is visible sunlight, with a similar amount of infrared radiation and 10 per cent ultraviolet.

As light is the form in which energy enters all but a few special kinds of autogenic natural systems, its intensity is of primary importance in determining the energy level at which any particular system can operate. The intensity of light also controls the locomotor activity of many lower organisms and the limited movements of plants. The selection of particular responses of cells to light intensity has led ultimately to the evolution of vision in higher animals.

The radiation intercepted by the Earth from a solar source that is of special concern to living systems on this planet lies in 400 to 760 millimicron wavelengths, what we describe as *sunlight*. This band provides the radiant energy for photosynthesis and thus directly drives all autotrophic ecosystems and indirectly also supplies the energy for heterotrophic ecosystems. Longer wavelengths, the *infrared* or *thermal radiation,* we can feel but not see. Nor is shorter solar radiation, the *ultraviolet,* visible to us directly, although some organisms—bees, for example—can clearly see it. Ultraviolet radiation has some detrimental effects on living systems, so that it is fortunate that much of it is absorbed by a layer of ozone in the atmosphere at a height of about 25 kilometers. Below this the atmosphere still absorbs ultraviolet radiation, although to a lesser extent. Thus, a mountain about five thousand meters high receives approximately twice the amount of ultraviolet radiation as that at sea level in the same region.

Many plants and animals respond to variations in the wavelength of incident light, utilizing some wave bands and being neutral to others. Of even greater ecological significance, however, is variation in the *duration* of light—the length of time between sunrise and sundown each day— which is known as the *photoperiod*. Between the equator and the polar circles, the photoperiod may vary with the season from nearly twenty-four hours to almost no time at all. In many temperate regions of the United States the photoperiod ranges from approximately six to as long as eighteen hours, summer occurring with the longer period and winter with the shorter.

This precisely definable and astronomically determined factor of the photoperiod is the most important ecological factor triggering seasonal reproductive behavior in animals and plants. The intensity of light required to evoke this photoperiodic response in plants is far below the compensation point. It appears, moreover, that in plants there is a delicate balance between the metabolic processes in the light and in the dark. Plants whose flowering is initiated by the onset of shorter days, which are known as short-day plants, could also be known as long-night plants, for if the dark interval is interrupted, they no longer respond. Flowering trees such as species of the genus *Erythrina* are sometimes planted as street trees in American cities near street lamps; either they never flower, because such species are short-day plants and the long spring and fall nights are always interrupted by the street lights, or they flower only intermittently as the new season's foliage shades the branches.

In Figure 2-10, the breeding behavior of the English sparrow at different latitudes is illustrated. Although some breeding occurs at the equator in every month, as one proceeds north and south into the Temperate Zones, breeding tends to be more and more restricted to the early summer months, that is, the time of year with the longest days. Beyond 50°N and 50°S sparrow breeding is restricted to the months of May and December, respectively. In the Temperate Zones, photoperiod is a major factor in restricting the breeding of birds to the months of the year when broods can be raised successfully. Being long-day breeders, birds are thus prevented from starting too early in the year or finishing too late to catch the warm summer months for raising their young.

The onsets of pairing in birds, mating in mammals, and spawning in fish are examples of animal reproductive processes that respond to photoperiod. Other behavioral patterns—for example, migration in birds and perhaps in some mammals such as the fur seal—are involved

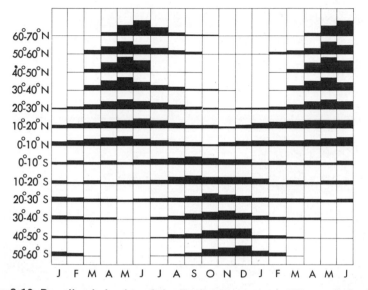

Figure 2-10. Breeding behavior of the English sparrow at different latitudes.
The graphs for each latitude show the relative intensity of breeding for each month; note that with increasing latitudes both north and south of the Equator, breeding tends to become restricted to the early summer months. After J. R. Baker, *Proceedings of The Zoological Society of London,* Series A, 108:559 (1938).

in photoperiod responses. These patterns will be discussed in later chapters.

Microenvironment

In addition to regional differences in climatic factors such as temperature and precipitation, local climatic variations are of considerable importance in limiting the distribution of organisms. For this phenomenon the term *microclimate* is still commonly employed, but it is better to use *microenvironment,* a term that is less than two decades old. Even this term, however, is still somewhat relative. It may include as large a volume as a layer of a forest (Figure 2-11), or it may refer to conditions within a single leaf (Figure 2-12).

The burrows of desert animals are an example of a microenvironment in which the physical parameters are quite different from those of the macroenvironment. The air the kangaroo rat breathes in his burrow has been shown to be from two to five times as humid as the desert air outside. It has been calculated that if a kangaroo rat had no burrow in which to escape from the daytime desert air, the rate of water loss in the respiratory air it expired would considerably exceed the water replenishment from its metabolic sources (the only source of water for a kangaroo rat) and the animal would soon die. Moreover, temperatures as low as 28°C have been

Figure 2-11. The microenvironment of shade-tolerant species of bromeliads in a tropical rain forest in Costa Rica. Other groups, such as epiphytic ferns and mosses, show similar stratification in relation to the forest microenvironments.

recorded within the burrows of these nocturnal animals when the diurnal surface temperature of the soil above exceeded 71°C.

A well-known microenvironmental effect is popularly used to determine the approximate compass direction in North Temperate Zone forests, that is, the fact that the side on which tree trunks are green is north. In the North Temperate Zone, low atmospheric moisture becomes a factor limiting the growth of lower organisms such as algae, liverworts, mosses, and lichens in the usually dry periods of later summer and early fall. The diurnal insolation of the south side of the trunks of forest trees raises temperatures, thereby increasing evaporation rates sufficiently to produce a microenvironment in which these lower organisms cannot survive, whereas it is believed that the lower temperatures on the north side of the trunks do not raise the evapotranspiration rates of the microhabitat sufficiently for them to become limiting.

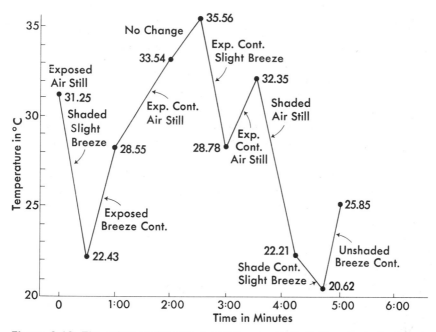

Figure 2-12. The microenvironment inside an oak leaf. The effect of external changes in air movement and light intensity is indicated by arrows. After R. B. Platt and J. N. Wolfe, *Plant Physiology*, 25:507–512 (1950).

Boundary Phenomena

    Microenvironmental factors may be considered to operate in an even more specific way as *boundary phenomena.* Indeed, if we take the conceptual position that all environmental interactions are fundamentally issues of energy exchange, then all population interactions with the physical and chemical features of the environment are boundary phenomena. This viewpoint has been especially developed in the United States by D. M. Gates, who has coined the term *teleoclimate* to refer to this critical boundary microenvironment.

    In population ecology boundary phenomena are particularly important in their critical modification of temperature parameters. For example, tolerance levels for critical temperature values are strongly modified by the degree of air disturbance. For plant populations this modification has been formalized by the development of an equation for the calculation of a *winter chill* factor. As in the case of animal populations, the effect of cold temperatures on plants is positively correlated with the extent of air movement. So too is the effect of high temperatures and low humidities. Both plant and animal populations frequently show adaptation, such as increased hairiness on their external surfaces, which are interpreted as conferring a wider tolerance range to such ecological factors by restriction of air movement.

Soil

The microenvironment and the macroenvironment contain numerous factors other than temperature and evaporation that affect the establishment, growth, and reproduction of animal, plant, and microbial populations. Some of these are the oxygen and carbon dioxide pressures, barometric pressure, and solar radiation. The area of the macroenvironment where such physical factors react with living organisms is known as the *biosphere,* which is described as being divided into the *hydrosphere,* including the atmosphere and the environmental factors just discussed, and the *pedosphere* or *lithosphere,* the soil.

The soil is the weathered layer of the Earth's crust with which living organisms and their products intermingle. Soils have three distinct but interdependent components. These are the parent mineral material derived from the underlying geological substrate, the dead and the living organic material supplied by the various populations in and on the soil, and the liquid and gaseous contents of the pores, or spaces, between particles—that is, the soil solution and the soil atmosphere. The size and nature of the particles of parent geological material and the amount of organic matter are of primary importance. Together they determine the availability of water and nutrients to the plant, animal, and microbial populations living in and on the soil, as well as the soil atmosphere in which the populations grow.

It will be apparent that soil can be regarded by an ecologist in a variety of ways. To a community ecologist soil is an immense and complex series of heterotrophic or heterogenic microecosystems, comparable with those of the ocean depths below the euphotic zone. These microecosystems can be investigated either as complete studies in themselves or with particular reference to the part they play in recycling the nutrients essential for terrestrial autotrophic or autogenic ecosystems. Or the soil can be regarded as a physical system, holding and making available for the animal, plant, and microbial populations that grow in or on it certain essential chemical substances, such as water, oxygen, and carbon dioxide. We now know that additionally it is a vast reservoir for a whole array of antibiotic and allelochemical substances.

For the purposes of this chapter, soil is regarded especially in the sense of a physical system and is described in terms of the ecological effect this system has on dependent animal and plant populations.

Soil Profiles

Soil scientists, or pedologists, classify variations in soil types on the basis of what is observed in a vertical section through the soil known as a soil profile (Figure 2-13). As revealed when a trench is dug, a soil profile shows a horizontal layering into what are known as *soil horizons.* Strictly speaking, it is the *sequence* of horizons in a soil that should be

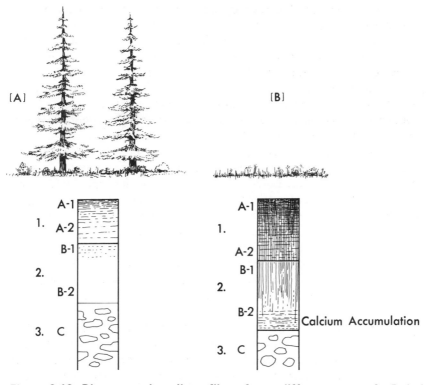

Figure 2-13. Diagrammatic soil profiles of two different types. A: Podzol developing in a high-rainfall area. B: Chernozem forming in an arid region. The three soil horizons *A, B,* and *C* vary in depth; the distribution of soluble ions, such as calcium, which are leached from the *A* horizon, is quite different in these contrasted soil-profile types.

described as its soil profile. The uppermost, or **A**, horizon contains the remains of plants and animals that are undergoing *humification*, that is, being converted into a largely inert homogeneous organic substance known as *humus*. The next lower, or **B**, horizon is composed of mineral soil. In the **B** horizon, humus and other organic materials have been converted into inorganic compounds by a process known as *mineralization*. Soluble material is often carried down, or *leached*, from the **A** horizon to lower horizons by the gravitational percolation of rainwater. The third, or **C**, horizon is formed of disintegrating parent rock material. The relative thickness of these three horizons in a soil profile characterizes particular climatic and topographical situations.

Soil Types

Soils are also grouped by pedologists on the basis of their mode of origin. In the United States, as over much of the Earth's surface, two major divisions are distinguished on this basis—the pedocal and the pedalfer soils.

The *pedocal* soils occur in the more arid regions, where rainfall is insufficient to percolate down to a water table. In the dry season, water is evaporated from the surface of the soil and soluble salts tend to accumulate in the **B** horizon rather than being leached away. The accumulation of calcium in particular (*ped-o-cal*) in the superficial layers of these soils ensures that the reaction will remain alkaline. One common type of pedocal soil is a *chernozem* (Figure 2-13), commonly known as black earth, which stretches southward in the United States from the Dakotas.

Pedalfer soils are found in the more humid regions. Leaching of the **A** horizon occurs and water filters through to the water table, from which many of the soil nutrients are eventually carried away. The colder and wetter regions of pedalfer soils have a particular type known as a *podzol* (Figure 2-13). Calcium is almost completely leached out of a podzol, which thus comes to have a highly acidic reaction. Aluminum and iron salts are also leached out of the **A** horizon (*ped-al-fer*) but tend to accumulate again in the **B** horizon as silicates. Whereas in a chernozem soil type fertility tends to be perpetuated, podzols become progressively more acid and infertile.

Under the cold and wet conditions of a podzol soil, humus tends to accumulate in a form known as *peat*. The effects of humus are perhaps better known than its composition and mode of formation; it combines with the finer clay particles to form a colloidal complex that confers many special characteristics on a soil. This colloidal complex increases the water-holding capacity of soils and slows down the rate of water and air movement; it also absorbs and holds the essential nutrients against leaching.

The soil factors that most affect the ecology of organisms are texture, that is, the relative proportions of different-sized particles such as sand, silt and clay; the humus content; the soil reaction, or pH; the amount of soil moisture and soil air; and the exchange capacity and degree of saturation, that is, the available minerals in the soil.

Nutrients

Organisms are divided on the basis of their mode of nutrition into autotrophs and heterotrophs. With certain exceptions not considered here, *autotrophs* are green plants, which directly synthesize their own food from its basic inorganic elements. *Heterotrophs* are animals or decomposing organisms, which can utilize only organic compounds for food; in other words, they must consume living or dead autotrophs or other heterotrophs.

Apart from carbon and oxygen, which autotrophs obtain from the air, green plants are almost exclusively dependent on the soil for the supply of the other thirty or so essential elements. The qualification is necessary because rainwater contains a limited but sometimes significant amount of dissolved substances, and some atmospheric nitrogen is fixed, that is, chemically incorporated in protoplasm, by microorganisms. The nutrients extracted from the soil by plants therefore represent the principal source of all essential elements except carbon and oxygen for populations of animals and aerobic microorganisms. Some nutrients are taken in by terrestrial animals in drinking water and in salt licks. In a marine environment the situation may be rather different; there is evidence that many marine invertebrates may extract at least some of the twenty or so known amino acids from seawater and utilize them directly.

Soil Nutrients

The nutrients available in the soil in the greatest amount are phosphate, nitrate, and sulfate salts of the elements calcium and potassium. Phosphates are not abundant; some are released during the weathering process of soil formation, but the largest source of supply of phosphates for plants is obtained by the breakdown of organic material in the soil. Although 78 per cent of the Earth's atmosphere is nitrogen gas, only certain bacteria can fix this gas; green plants commonly obtain their required nitrogen from nitrates in the soil, also usually released during the breakdown of organic material. Some plants can absorb nitrogen in other forms, such as ammonium salts; certain algae can absorb it in nitrite and amino acid form also. Sulfates are abundant in the soil and the sea, and never in limiting quantities.

Calcium occurs in soils as lime, or calcium carbonate. The amount present depends upon the combined action of climatic and biological weathering on the basic rock material and upon its original composition. In soils with an acid reaction, cations of calcium tend to be replaced by hydrogen ions and the calcium is leached away. Soil processes in such calcium-deficient soils differ from those in soils that are calcium-rich, and some plants are restricted in their occurrence to one or the other type of soil. Potassium salts are derived during the weathering of rocks, being released in soluble form from the complex potassium silicates that generally occur in all rock material.

Trace elements such as iron, zinc, boron, and copper usually occur in soils and natural waters in sufficient quantity not to be limiting but may become so in exceptional cases. The minuteness of the amounts involved in plant growth may be illustrated by the fact that 1 part in 200 million parts of zinc will have a detectable effect.

Because the amounts of the elements phosphorus, nitrogen, and potassium are frequently the limiting factor in cropped soils, considerable commercial success has been obtained by the addition of mixtures of these elements to agricultural soils in the form, usually, of potassium phosphates and ammonium sulfate. Much less experimental work has been carried out on the need for trace elements in farm land, but boron and cobalt in particular have been shown to be limiting in some soils.

Lake Nutrients

As in the case of soils, the nutrients available in fresh water vary considerably from lake to lake and may show wide variation both in depth and by season. On a basis of differences in the availability of nutrients, lakes have been classified as oligotrophic, eutrophic, and dystrophic. *Oligotrophic* lakes are deep and are deficient in NPK and dissolved organic materials, but the oxygen content is high at all levels. *Eutrophic* lakes are somewhat shallow and are rich in NPK, organic matter, and other nutrients; the oxygen content suffers seasonal depletion. *Dystrophic* lakes are peaty, with plentiful NPK and organic matter; the high concentrations of humic substances cause oxygen depletion and prevent utilization of the nutrients.

Nutrients and Animals

Being heterotrophic, animals require as food such organic substances as carbohydrates, proteins, fats, and certain salts and accessory substances such as vitamins. Deficiencies in food may relate either to its scarcity or to its composition. Although there is considerable flexibility as to the balance of these various substances, some protein intake is required for growth and for the repair of damaged tissues in animals. Moreover, the composition of the animal's food is determined by whether its way of life is herbivorous or carnivorous. Some herbivores have a dentition permitting them to graze or browse on plants and also a gastric system that can digest plant material especially well. Thus the group of mammals known as *ruminants* has a special system of stomachs assisting grass digestion. This is achieved through a mutualistic association with protozoa in the rumen. These protozoa digest the cellulose-plant cell walls and so make the cell contents available to the ruminants. Other herbivores such as aphids, which can feed directly on the amino acids of their hosts, and scale insects have special sucking mouthparts. Such specialization is less common among carnivores, although they may develop such habits as bloodsucking; this habit is developed in ticks, insects, and leeches.

The distribution of animals, on either a general or a local scale, is related to the occurrence of their specific kind of food in or on particular soils. Pronghorn antelope are grazers and therefore occur on the plains, where they are clearly visible to predators. Smaller animals are limited to those microhabitats in which fluctuations in microenvironment do not exceed their limits of tolerance and are still further restricted to favorable microenvironments in which their specific food requirements do not become limiting.

Soil Disturbances

Disturbance of a soil profile can have profound and even disastrous results for the living organisms associated with it. One of the most spectacular demonstrations of this occurred in the middlewestern wheat states, especially Kansas and Oklahoma, in the 1930s. Rapid and extensive increases in the ploughing-up of grassland for the cultivation of wheat, made possible by the changeover from horse to tractor power and stimulated by good wheat prices, caused widespread disturbance in the soil profile. Much of the disturbed section of the soil profile, no longer being stabilized by a natural grass cover, was liable to blow away in great dust storms in the drier seasons of the year. The resulting dust-bowl conditions have been well documented in scientific works and dramatically described in such novels as John Steinbeck's *The Grapes of Wrath.*

Fire

Although catastrophes on such a scale as the 1930s' dust-bowl calamity could not occur without human interference, soil has always been subject to the effects of certain more local disturbances, such as floods, avalanches, landslides, rockfalls, and, especially, fires.

Even before the advent of man, periodic fires started by lightning strikes or volcanic action must have occurred in all areas except the more perpetually wet forms of tropical rain forest. It is possible that some plants and animals—for example, those found in chaparral—have evolved in association with fire as an ecological factor and require this factor if they are to achieve an equilibrium. Some coniferous species—for example, lodgepole pine (*Pinus contorta*) and the closely related jack pine (*P. banksiana*)—do not freely release their seeds from the persistent cones until fire has swept over them; they therefore spring up in large numbers only after forest fires. There are whole continents, such as Australia, and whole tropical areas, such as the African savanna, where all recent evolution has been in an environment subjected to annual fires. There are many other large areas—such as the boreal forest, which stretches over northern Canada, Northern Europe, and Russia, and the ponderosa forests of the western United States (Figure 2-14)—where local fires have probably recurred at intervals of perhaps twenty to one hundred years.

Nevertheless, fire as a major destructive ecological factor has reached its present preeminence only with the assistance of man. It is conceivable that early forms of our species, *Homo sapiens,* and our more immediate fire-utilizing ancestors could never have achieved great hunting success

Figure 2-14. Tendency of periodic fires in the ponderosa (yellow) pine forests of the western United States to produce even-aged stands of trees. A: Accumulation of flammable debris in a mature regenerating forest. **B:** Occurrence of lightning or man-made fire, killing all seedlings. **C:** Growth of seedlings into young trees during period of reduced fire hazard, suppressing the growth of further seedlings.

without the use of fire. Certainly agriculture could not have developed in the tropical world without the use of fire for clearing vegetation and providing nutrients for crop growth, as illustrated in Table 2-3.

The slash-and-burn method of clearing tropical woody vegetation, which anthropologists now call *swidden agriculture* when it is associated with shifting cultivation, demonstrably releases large quantities of nutrients, but the soil and vegetation take fifteen to fifty years to recover before the operation can be repeated.

This chapter on the physical and chemical factors that affect populations has outlined the extent of the interaction between plants and animals and the abiotic environment. Other chapters explore how these factors influence the distribution, growth, and reproduction of populations. The companion volume on community ecology describes how these factors

Table 2-3. Estimated Quantities of Nutrients Released by the Burning of Tropical Vegetation (in pounds per acre)

	Phosphate	Potassium	Calcium	Magnesium
Tropical rain forest (forty years old)	112	731	2,254	309
Savanna woodland	20	171	241	79

After P. H. Nye, *Tropical Soils and Vegetation,* UNESCO Abidjan Symposium, 1959, pp. 59–63.

operate on community energetics and modify ecosystem development and function.

References and Further Readings

ANSLEY, E. "How Air Pollution Alters Weather." *New Scientist,* 44:66–67 (1969).

BATCHELDER, R. B., and H. F. HIRT. "Fire in Tropical Forests and Grasslands." *U.S. Army Natick Laboratories Technical Report,* 67-41-ES, 1966.

BECK, S. D. "Insects and the Length of Day." *Scientific American,* 202(2):108–118 (1960).

BILLINGS, W. D., and H. A. MOONEY. "The Ecology of Arctic and Alpine Plants." *Biological Review,* 43:481–529 (1968).

BOUGHEY, A. S. "The Vegetation Types of Southern Rhodesia." *Proceedings and Transactions of the Rhodesia Scientific Association,* 49:54–98 (1961).

BOWEN, H. J. M. *Trace Elements in Biochemistry.* New York: Academic Press, Inc., 1966.

BUTLER, W. L., and R. J. DOWNS. "Light and Plant Development." *Scientific American,* 203(6):56–63 (1960).

CLOUDSLEY-THOMPSON, J. L. *Microecology.* New York: St. Martin's Press, Inc., 1967.

COOPER, C. E. "The Ecology of Fire." *Scientific American,* 204(4):150–160 (1961).

CROWE, J. H., and A. F. COOPER. "Cryptobiosis." *Scientific American,* 225(6):30–36 (1971).

DAUBENMIRE, R. F. "Climate as a Determinant of Vegetation Distribution in Eastern Washington and Northern Idaho." *Ecological Monographs,* 26:131–154 (1956).

DEEVEY, E. S. "Mineral Cycles." *Scientific American,* 223(30):149–158 (1970).

EDNEY, E. B. "Water Balance in Desert Anthropods." *Science,* 156:1059–1066 (1967).

FRAENKEL, G. S. "The Heat Resistance of Intertidal Snails." *Physiological Zoology,* 41:1–13 (1968).

GATES, D. M. *Man and His Environment: Climate.* New York: Harper & Row, Publishers, 1972.

HARE, F. K. *The Restless Atmosphere.* London: Hutchinson & Co., Ltd., 1966.

HUDSON, J. W. "Variations in the Patterns of Torpidity of Small Homeotherms." In *Mammalian Hibernation,* Vol. 3, K. C. Fisher (ed.) New York: American Elsevier Publishing Co., Inc., 1967, pp. 30–46.

JACKSON, R. M., and F. RAW. *Life in Soil.* New York: St. Martin's Press, Inc., 1966.

KENNERLY, T. E. "Microenvironmental Conditions of the Pocket Gopher Burrow." *Texas Journal of Science,* 16:395–441 (1964).

LOWE, C. H., and D. S. HINDS. "Effect of Paloverde (*Cercidium*) Trees on the Radiation Flux." *Ecology,* 52:916–922 (1971).

MACMILLEN, R. E., and A. K. LESS. "Australian Desert Mice: Independence of Exogenous Water." *Science,* 158:383–385 (1967).

PENMAN, H. L. "The Water Cycle." *Scientific American,* 223(3):98–108 (1970).

PORTER, W. P., and D. M. GATES. "Thermodynamic Equilibria of Animals with Environment." *Ecological Monographs,* 39:227–244 (1960).

SCHMIDT-NIELSEN, K. "The Physiology of the Camel." *Scientific American,* 201(6):140–151 (1959).

SCHMIDT-NIELSEN, K. "Comparative Morphology and Physiology of Excretion." In *Ideas in Modern Biology*, J. A. Moore (ed.) Garden City, N.Y.: Natural History Press, 1965.

SCHOLANDER, P. E., R. HOCK, V. WALTERS, F. JOHNSON, and L. IRVING. "Heat Regulation in Some Arctic and Tropical Mammals and Birds." *Biological Bulletin*, 99:237–258 (1950).

STUDIER, E. H., and T. P. BACA. "Atmospheric Conditions in Artificial Rodent Burrows." *Southwestern Naturalist*, 13:401–410 (1968).

SUTCLIFFE, J. *Plants and Water*. New York: St. Martin's Press, Inc., 1968.

THORNTHWAITE, C. W. "An Approach to a Rational Classification of Climate." *Geographical Review*, 38:55–94 (1958).

WAGGONER, P. E., and W. E. REIFSNYDER. "Simulation of the Microclimate in a Forest." *Forest Science*, 15:37–45 (1969).

———, and I. ZELITCH. "Transpiration and the Stomata of Leaves." *Science*, 150:1413–1420 (1965).

WENT, F. W. "Climate and Agriculture." *Scientific American*, 196(6):82–94 (1957).

WOODWELL, G. M. "Radiation and the Patterns of Nature." *Science*, 156:461–470 (1967).

Chapter 3 • Population Evolution

So far we have considered only the characteristics and interactions of populations to the extent that they are *proximate,* that is, their effects are immediately apparent. There remains the *ultimate,* or long-term, modification of populations produced by the continuing operation of particular abiotic environmental factors. The sustained pressure produces changes in the environmental requirements of a population when it causes a progressive directional change in the gene frequencies of the population. The consequent adaptation of biological characteristics and physical and chemical requirements constitutes the genetic process known as *evolution.* The essential basis for this process is *biotic variation,* without which evolution could not occur.

Variation

Individual members of a population are never completely identical; in one manner or another each individual varies, however minutely, from all other members of the population.

Within a species, variation may come about in two different but interrelated ways. It may originate from differences in the genetic complement, or *genome,* of different individuals. Directional selection then operates on this *genotypic variation* within the species population, modifying the gene frequencies of its many alleles to effect evolution. Or variation may be produced by exposure to different values for particular environmental parameters during the development of individuals possessing similar genomes; this second type of variation is commonly termed *phenotypic variation.* In *phenotypic variation* individual organisms may adapt, or *acclimate,* in response to specific changes in environmental factors. Sometimes, especially when the phenotypic response has occurred in the developmental stage of the organism, the variation may be fixed. Frequently it is not, and as has already been noted, many animals can repeatedly acclimate to varying temperature ranges. Other environmental factors commonly associated with phenotypic variation are light intensity and atmospheric humidity. Generally speaking, such variation is not inherited and is not a basis for evolution.

Mutation and Recombination

Genotypic variation, on which selection pressures operate to bring about evolution, arises basically from two causes, mutation and recombination. Fundamentally, however, these are not discrete processes. Without mutation and the formation of new alleles, there would not be any crossing over and segregation in meiosis and recombination after fertilization.

Molecular biologists have now demonstrated that genetic information is conveyed from one generation to another as developmental instructions coded on DNA molecules. In DNA duplication during gene replication at nuclear division, as in any biological process, random errors occur, resulting in the genetic changes that are known as mutations. What is actually involved is a substitution of one nucleotide pair for another in the DNA molecule. The great majority of mutations are not a unique occurrence, but are repeated at varying intervals of time, which are determined by the calculation of the *mutation rate.* With the exception only of those with extremely low mutation rates, all mutations are reversible. Most are detrimental to the development, survival, and reproduction of the organism that develops from the genome containing the mutation. For this reason mutations are usually recessive, for an individual carrying a dominant detrimental mutant is unlikely to survive.

Failure of the gene-copying process during nuclear division is not the only cause of mutation. There may be structural displacements of portions of chromosomes. Also, in many species the mutation rate is known to be controlled by a group of mutator genes and is therefore subject to control by natural selection. The mutation rate of any particular gene may be affected by a number of environmental factors as well as by the mutator genes. The Nobel prize was awarded to the American geneticist H. J. Muller some years ago for demonstrating that x-ray bombardment of sex cells results in an increased number of mutations. Other forms of electromagnetic waves, like cosmic rays, and many chemical substances, such as mustards and purines, have the same result.

The British geneticist R. A. Fisher explained why mutations are almost invariably detrimental. He argued that when a population is nearly perfectly adapted to its habitat, and virtually all natural populations are, it has little chance of being improved by a mutation involving any substantial change in its structure or behavior. By analogy, if a camera is nearly perfectly focused, a considerable change cannot improve it, and only a very small change has a fifty-fifty chance of putting it into better focus.

In a given population, alleles that do not contribute to the survival of individual genotypes, or rather to the survival of the individuals possessing these genotypes, will tend to be eliminated. Simultaneously with this loss, new nonessential or deleterious alleles are being added to the gene pool of the population by mutation and by introgression from adjoining populations. In a sexually reproducing species, these new genes are constantly being shuffled during gamete formation and gamete fusion in the process known as *recombination*. Genomes containing the recombined genes are subject to continuing selection so that evolution proceeds, at rates varying with the selection pressures, the mutation and introgression rates, and the extent of recombination, by a constant and continual series of changes in gene frequency.

Gene Frequency

The amount of variation apparent in a population is thus a mere fraction of its total potential genetic variability. Sexual animal populations and all outbreeding plants contain a hidden store of variability in the form of recessive alleles that can be brought to light only by chance or by inbreeding. There are several reasons why this great store of variation exists. First, unfavorable recessive mutations will not start to be eliminated until their frequency becomes sufficiently high for homozygotes of this condition to appear. Heterozygotes will not be eliminated from the population. Second, if an unfavorable mutation occurs near the locus of a gene with high selective value, the mutant will tend to be selected with the favorable allele because of its very low crossing-over frequency.

As has been noted, new alleles are introduced into populations not only by mutation but also by introgression, that is, by the entrance of genes from other populations. Basically, the alleles obtained by introgression also have in their turn been provided by mutation. In a large species population, when mating occurs at random, no further changes can occur in gene frequency without the occurrence or introduction of other mutations, on the one hand, or a variation in the operation of a particular selection pressure, on the other. This may be demonstrated as follows. In such a population

$$p + q = 1$$

where

$$p = \text{frequency of allele } A_1$$
$$q = \text{frequency of allele } A_2$$

In a random combination, these two alleles will give the following genotypes and gene frequencies:

$$A_1A_1 \quad p \times p = p^2$$
$$A_1A_2 \quad p \times q = pq$$
$$A_2A_1 \quad q \times p = qp$$
$$A_2A_2 \quad q \times q = q^2$$

As the genotypes A_1A_2 and A_2A_1 are identical, their combined frequency is $2pq$. In the F_2 (second generation), the homozygotes will give
only one kind of gamete and the heterozygotes will yield the two possibilities in equal numbers, as follows:

$$\text{proportion of } A_1 \text{ gametes}: p^2 + \tfrac{1}{2} 2pq = p(p + q) = p$$
$$\text{proportion of } A_2 \text{ gametes}: q^2 + \tfrac{1}{2} 2pq = q(q + p) = q$$

Therefore the frequency of A_1 and A_2 gametes in the F_2 following
random mating without selection is the same as in the F_1 gametes that
produced it. The proportion of the two alleles in the genotypes of successive generations will not change, so that with continuing random
mating in a large population without selection pressure, the expectation is that the initial variability will be maintained. This expectation is
known as the *Hardy-Weinberg law*.

The change that mutation alone can introduce into a population at
the Hardy-Weinberg equilibrium is very low. Some mutations are so
rare as to be almost unique. As has already been noted, the majority are
recurrent and reversible, and their expected gene frequency can be
calculated mathematically. If an allele A_1 mutates to A_2, the frequency
of A_2 in the following generation can be expressed as

$$p_0 - (u \times p_0)$$

where

$$u = \text{mutation rate of } A_1$$
$$p_0 = \text{initial frequency of } A_1$$
$$u \times p_0 = \text{decrease in frequency of } A_1$$

If there are 1 million gametes with the A_1 allele and their mutation
rate u is 10^{-5}, the following calculations result from substitution:

$$p_0 = 1$$
$$u \times p_0 = 10^{-5} \times 1 = 0.00001$$

The new frequency of A_1 is

$$p_0 - (u \times p_0) = 1 - 0.00001 = 0.99999$$

Thus, after one generation, there will be 999,990 gametes with the allele A_1 and 10 with A_2.

But the mutation is reversible; that is, there is *back mutation*. As the frequency of the second allele increases, fewer of the first are left to mutate but more of the second are available for the back mutation. An equilibrium is eventually achieved at which there will be no further *frequency* change as a result of mutation; the frequency of the allele A_1 will depend entirely on the rate at which it mutates to A_2 and back again.

Natural Selection

The process that operates on gene frequencies to determine the balance of what in effect is a pool of mutations is known as *natural selection*. Under field conditions there is a continuous interaction between the phenotypes of individuals in the population and the environment. Especially when the population migrates or there is a change in the environment, a selection of phenotypes with the genomes containing different ratios of mutant alleles develops. This process of natural selection was first well documented by Charles Darwin in his classic work *On the Origin of Species*, published in 1859.

Hardy-Weinberg equilibrium is not usual under natural conditions. A new mutant allele causes a varying disturbance to the phenotype developing from the genotype that includes it, depending to some extent on its interaction with the other alleles. Some mutants are completely recessive in certain genotypes but deleterious in others. Thus when a value for *fitness*—that is, a selection value—is assigned to a particular mutant, this value is its average fitness in the whole population.

The case of complete dominance, where a mutant allele is selected against only when it is in the homozygous condition, is the simplest to consider. By the Hardy-Weinberg law the frequencies of the three possible genome combinations are

$$A_1 A_1 \qquad p^2$$
$$A_1 A_2 \qquad 2pq$$
$$A_2 A_2 \qquad q^2$$

Thus

$$p^2 + 2pq + q^2 = 1$$

and the fitnesses of the three genome combinations are

$$A_1A_1 \quad 1$$
$$A_1A_2 \quad 1$$
$$A_2A_2 \quad 1 - s$$

where s is the coefficient of selection against the homozygous recessive.

The respective gametic contribution will therefore be the product of the frequency and the fitness of each genome combination; that is,

$$\text{contribution of } A_1A_1 = p^2 \times 1$$
$$\text{contribution of } A_1A_2 = 2pq \times 1$$
$$\text{contribution of } A_2A_2 = q^2 \times (1 - s)$$

In order to determine the frequency of the mutant allele A_2 in the succeeding generation (q_1), one half of the A_1A_2 contribution plus the A_2A_2 contribution must be divided by the new total of gametic contributions, which is $1 - sq^2$, giving

$$q_1 = \frac{pq + q^2(1 - s)}{1 - sq^2}$$

The change in one generation resulting from selection is

$$\Delta q = q_1 - q = \frac{pq + q^2(1 - s)}{1 - sq^2} - q$$

which simplifies to

$$\Delta q = \frac{-sq^2(1 - q)}{1 - sq^2}$$

The same rationale is employed to determine the selection effect in other circumstances, such as when there is overdominance or when both alleles are selected against in the homozygous condition. The resulting formulas for these several circumstances are listed in Table 3-1. The changes in gene frequency under two of these circumstances are illustrated graphically in Figure 3-1.

By a similar argument, a simplified expression for the gene frequency of a mutant when mutation and selection are balanced can be obtained. It is

$$q^2 = \frac{u}{s}$$

As the more usual values for mutation rates lie between 10^{-4} and 10^{-8} gametes, it can be seen from this expression that the frequency of a

Table 3-1. Selection Effects

Conditions of Dominance and Selection	Fitness of Genotypes			Change of Frequency of Gene A_2
	A_1A_1 (initial frequency p^2)	A_1A_2 (initial frequency $2pq$)	A_2A_2 (initial frequency q^2)	
No dominance— selection against A_2	1	$1 - \frac{1}{2}s$	$1 - s$	$-\dfrac{\frac{1}{2}sq(1-q)}{1-sq}$
Complete dominance—selection against A_2A_2	1	1	$1 - s$	$-\dfrac{sq^2(1-q)}{1-sq^2}$
Complete dominance—selection against A_1	$1 - s$	$1 - s$	1	$+\dfrac{sq^2(1-q)}{1-s(1-q^2)}$
Overdominance— selection against A_1A_1 and A_2A_2	$1 - s_1$	1	$1 - s_2$	$+\dfrac{pq(s_1p-s_2q)}{1-s_1p^2-s_2q^2}$

After D. S. Falconer, *Introduction to Quantitative Genetics* (Edinburgh, Scotland: Oliver and Boyd, Ltd., 1961).

mutant allele will be kept low even without selection pressure against it. However, even if there is selection pressure against it in the homozygous condition, the allele at this low level must exist only in the heterozygous condition and is not likely to be significantly deleterious. Natural populations can thus contain a large number of low-level disadvantageous recessive mutant alleles that cannot be eliminated from the population. This is often described as the *genetic load* of a population. It is natural selection that will determine whether or not, with environmental changes, any of the alleles in this genetic load will spread through the population in response to new demands.

MacArthur and Connell have drawn an apt analogy between natural selection and bank or stock investments. If an investor deposits some silver and some paper money in a bank that pays 5 per cent annual interest on the former and 4 per cent on the latter and the interest is paid in the same form of money as the original investment, silver produces silver and paper produces paper. The amount of silver money in the bank will increase faster than the paper. In biological terms, silver is fitter than paper, so the silver/paper ratio increases; silver has the advantage by differential reproduction, as it were.

If one applies this analogy, differences in *phenotypes* can be described, just as can differences in *fitness,* by their comparative ability to leave

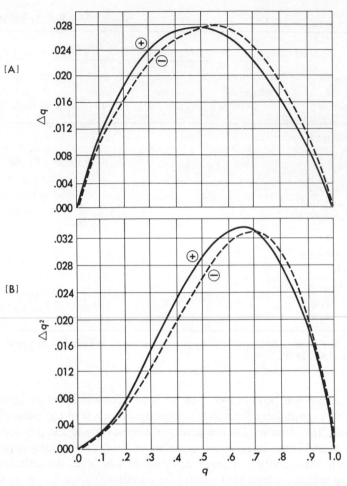

Figure 3-1. Change of gene frequency Δq under selection of intensity $S = 0.2$ at different values of initial frequency q. A: A gene with no dominance. **B:** A gene with complete dominance. In both cases a continuous line refers to selection in favor of the gene, so that Δq is positive; the dotted line refers to selection against the gene whose frequency is q, so that Δq is negative. After D. S. Falconer, *Introduction to Quantitative Genetics* (Edinburgh, Scotland: Oliver and Boyd, Ltd., 1960), p. 31.

descendants. That *most different phenotypes have different fitnesses* is the first empirical fact of natural selection. The second empirical fact is that *most phenotypes are sufficiently hereditary.* These two facts are the essential basis of natural selection; they require that hereditably fitter characteristics are constantly replacing the less fit.

In Darwin's *Origin of Species*, natural selection was a deduction supported by circumstantial evidence. Since it was written, it has become possible to demonstrate by experiments the operation of natural selection in populations. The most commonly cited experimental work on this point was performed on the peppered moth (*Biston betularia*), which in industrial Britain within a century changed from populations with mostly white forms to populations with mostly black forms. The black forms in a population previously believed to be white were first noticed about 1850. The black forms of moth were commonest where industrial fumes had killed lichens on tree trunks, making the trunks appear darker; hence the phenomenon is now usually known as *industrial melanism*. By the turn of the century the melanistic forms had become predominant in a number of industrial areas.

In an experiment H. B. D. Kettlewell marked moths of both forms; these were released in woods both in the vicinity of industry and far from it. Kettlewell subsequently recaptured more light moths in the distant, unaffected woods and more dark moths in the industrial woods. This effectively demonstrated the selective value of color in bird predation on the moths. The actual figures obtained in the experiment are listed in Table 3-2.

Such circumstances as the onset of industrial melanism in the peppered moth are rather unusual; most animal and plant species are well adapted to their environment. Major changes in gene frequencies due to natural selection are especially the result of disturbance to particular ecosystems, such as the removal of predators in animal populations and the clearing of land in plant communities.

Maintenance of Variation

It might be imagined that natural selection would gradually eliminate all variation from a population, leaving only one allele at each locus. In fact, it is known that there are several ways of storing genetic variability. For example, in a population with recurring recessive mutation at one particular locus, the action of natural selection and the reverse mutation

Table 3-2. Recapture Data on Dark and Light Moths

	Dark Woods (near Birmingham)			Light Woods (in Dorset)		
	Dark	Light	Total	Dark	Light	Total
Number of moths not recaptured	72	48	120	443	434	877
Number of moths recaptured	82	16	98	30	62	92
Total number of moths released	154	64	218	473	496	969

Data from H. B. D. Kettlewell, *Annual Review of Entomology*, 6:245–262 (1961).

will balance the mutation rate. Thus hemophilia, a sex-linked human allele that causes heterozygous males and homozygous females to bleed freely, is maintained by a mutation rate that counterbalances the elimination of unfit bleeders.

In certain instances a heterozygous genotype is fitter than either homozygote. Then if either allele becomes rare, it is most likely to recombine with the other allele in a heterozygous and therefore fitter genotype. The most frequently quoted example of this circumstance is the human variant known as *sickle-cell anemia,* in which the hemoglobin structure is modified so that a homozygote for the condition usually dies of anemia in childhood. On the other hand, it appears that the heterozygote has some considerable tolerance to attacks of malaria. In areas of Africa where the incidence of malaria is high, that is, particularly around the forest-savanna ecotone, the sickle-cell gene reaches a high level in the human populations. If this were because of a high mutation rate, the level would not drop in populations removed to nonmalarial areas. However, people of African descent in the United States show a lower frequency of the gene, which may be expected to drop until it balances the mutation rate. Although this hemoglobin polymorphism occurs with highest frequency in Africa, it does occur elsewhere in the Old World, correlated with the known distribution of malaria (Figure 3-2).

J. B. S. Haldane has postulated that an average of approximately thirty selective deaths per individual genome are required before an unfit genotype is eliminated. Thus if an average of one tenth of a selective death per individual genome per generation has occurred during evolutionary time, one allele will be eliminated in every three hundred generations. However, isolation, for example on an island, may cause immediate elimination of alleles. Whatever alleles of the mainland population are not present in the isolated population, either in the homozygous or heterozygous condition, will be immediately lost.

The ratio of males and females in a population is a good illustration of the balancing of alleles. The males as a group make roughly the same contribution to the genotypes of the population as the females. If there are half as many males as females, and assuming that no females remain unmated, a male will contribute twice as much to the offspring as a female. This will tend to restore the sex balance until the numbers of males and females are approximately equal, as they are in most animal populations.

Figure 3-2. Comparison of the distribution in the Old World of the allele for sickle-cell anemia (A) with the occurrence of malaria (B). Mortality among infants and young children is especially high in those areas of Africa in which malaria and the sickle-cell trait are high, but the correlation between the occurrence of the trait and the incidence of the disease is complicated by the fact that infant mortality in these areas undoubtedly arises from a variety of causes. After J. Buettner-Janusch, *Origins of Man* (New York: John Wiley & Sons, Inc., 1966), pp. 539, 542.

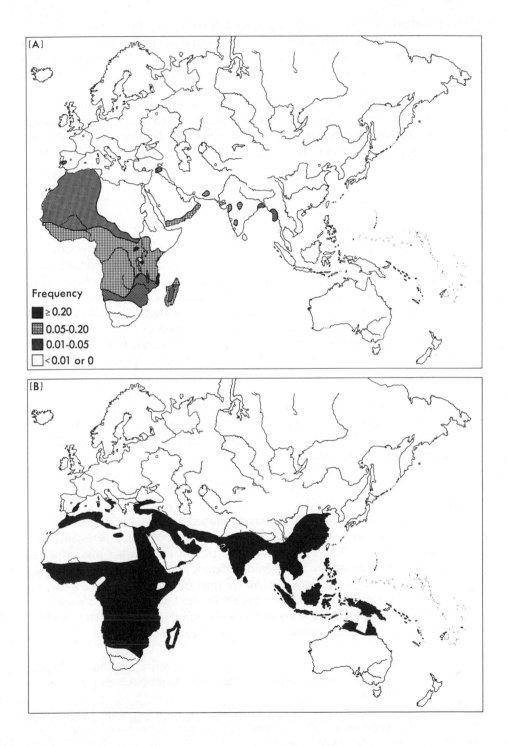

[A]

Frequency
■ ≥ 0.20
▦ 0.05–0.20
▨ 0.01–0.05
□ <0.01 or 0

[B]

Group Selection

Most species have a fair to large area of distribution and occur in discrete but not completely isolated populations, often of the kind described as demes or as subspecies in animals, and ecotypes in plants. When one of these local discrete populations has decreased in numbers until it is no longer viable, *local extinction* takes place. Other populations, by contrast, never show this phenomenon of local extinction; they are less subject to the total extinction that occurs when all the discrete populations, through some widespread disaster, are subject simultaneously to local extinction.

Clines

When a population is exposed to an environmental gradient, there will be a corresponding gradient in selection pressures. Increasing values of the particular environment factor along the gradient will produce correspondingly increased values in selection pressure. Such a gradient of biotypes, or races, within a population is known as a *cline;* the term *cline* was originally suggested by the English biologist Sir Julian Huxley, grandson of Darwin's advocate, Thomas Huxley. The distinguished American geneticist Ledyard Stebbins has postulated that it is probable that most species with a continuous range that includes more than one altitudinal or latitudinal climatic belt will possess clines of physiological features adapting them to the particular characteristics of their habitat range. His prediction has already been confirmed in a number of observations and experiments, such as those concerned with variation in leaf glaucosity, a factor that would appear to have no immediate selection value in a normal environment.

Ecotypes

The concept of the ecotype was developed by the Swedish genocologist G. Turesson as a result of a series of observations and experiments conducted in the 1920s and 1930s on variation in Swedish plant species. Turesson collected live plants from different parts of the country and grew them together in the same garden. He thus started a procedure for transplant experiments that has since been followed by many genecologists—or *biosystematists,* as they are now more commonly called.

Turesson's basic conclusions may be expressed as follows:

1. Widely distributed species exhibit a variation in morphological and physiological characters; these vary from place to place within the habitat.
2. This variation is largely correlated with observable habitat differences.

3. This correlated variation, where it is not simply phenotypic variation, is the result of the natural selection of particular genotypes from the pool of genetic variability available within the species.

The population sampling and subsequent cultivation procedures that Turesson followed led him to conclude that species were composed of a mosaic of populations—the ecotypes—each adapted by natural selection to a particular habitat and each being discontinuously distinct from the others. Thus populations of ecotypes were seen to differ from clinal populations, in which variation is both continuous and directional.

More recent studies, such as those of J. W. Gregor, have shown that Turesson's methods were wrong insofar as they led him to postulate discontinuous variation exclusively. There can also be continuously varying ecotypes; the term *ecocline* is sometimes used for such populations. An ecotype in this case becomes a particular range on an ecocline.

The most serious criticism of Turesson's work is that cultivation of ecotypes in one uniform area could obscure genetically determined differences in adaption to particular environments. Turesson's simple transplant experiments were greatly improved upon in the now-classical experiments of J. Clausen, D. D. Keck, and W. M. Hiesey, using a transect from the California shore to the Sierra Nevada Mountains with a series of transplant stations along it. These investigators studied a number of species containing distinct and discontinuous ecological races (Figure 3-3). Their work may be summarized as concluding that individuals within local populations of a widespread species differ in minor but distinguishable morphological and physiological characters and that populations from climatically distinct regions are to a greater degree divergent morphologically and physiologically and represent ecotypes.

It is apparent that ecotypes segregate from a population through selection pressures of several different kinds. In Gregor's work the ecotypes are adapted to varying edaphic conditions, whereas the California work of Clausen, Keck, and Hiesey deals mostly with climatic ecotypes. The operation of any ecological factor or any combination of factors, in fact, can lead to the selection of ecotypes. The factors can conveniently be classified here as climatic, edaphic, and biotic.

CLIMATIC ECOTYPES   The occurrence of climatic ecotypes has been discussed by C. McMillan, who points out that it has been shown that in fifteen out of seventeen species in eight of nine American tree genera examined (*Acer, Betula, Fraxinus, Larix, Picea, Prunus, Pseudotsuga,* and *Ulmus*), photoperiod ecotypes could be correlated with the latitude of seed origin. H. A. Mooney and W. D. Billings (1961) worked on *Oxyria digyna*, which occurs from as far north in North America as the arctic tundra at 83°N to the mountains of Arizona in the south. They demonstrated that there is a close adjustment to the specific light climate of the

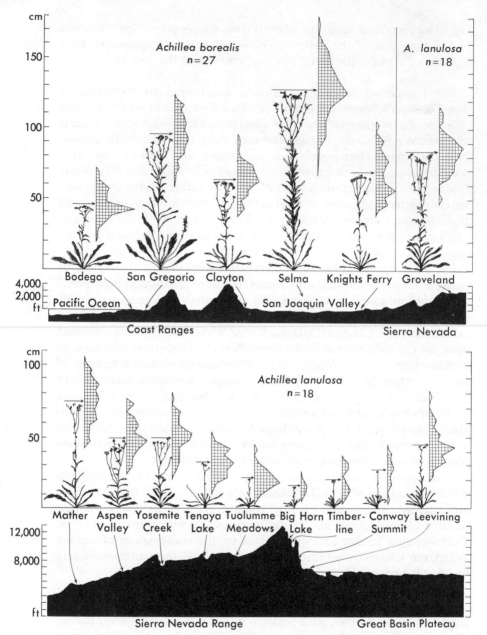

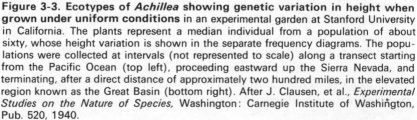

Figure 3-3. Ecotypes of *Achillea* showing genetic variation in height when grown under uniform conditions in an experimental garden at Stanford University in California. The plants represent a median individual from a population of about sixty, whose height variation is shown in the separate frequency diagrams. The populations were collected at intervals (not represented to scale) along a transect starting from the Pacific Ocean (top left), proceeding eastward up the Sierra Nevada, and terminating, after a direct distance of approximately two hundred miles, in the elevated region known as the Great Basin (bottom right). After J. Clausen, et al., *Experimental Studies on the Nature of Species,* Washington: Carnegie Institute of Washington, Pub. 520, 1940.

habitat of each population. Thus, whereas photoperiod response is a frequent factor in climatic-ecotype selection, ecotypes selected for temperature responses are also common. Response to temperature may be immediate or latent and is usually complex and difficult to analyze, being compounded from both short-term (that is, day-and-night) and long-term (that is, seasonal) temperature ranges.

A rather special type of climatic-ecotype class occurs along seacoasts, especially subtropical and tropical seacoasts. Salt spray from breaking waves may be blown inland from distances of several hundred meters, as may be observed on the windshield of any car parked near a California or Florida beach. The salt deposits are toxic to the shoot initials of flowering plants. There is therefore a selection pressure for prostrate ecotypes, which produce a plant form over which the salt spray passes harmlessly.

EDAPHIC ECOTYPES   Edaphic ecotypes occur especially in saline soils and serpentine soils, but also in response to soil-moisture stress, a factor perhaps not dissociable from climatic effects. A. R. Kruckeberg states that a major criterion of tolerance for serpentine soil appears to be the ability to tolerate low calcium levels. Comparing the tolerances of serpentine and nonserpentine ecotypes of *Phacelia californica* for calcium deficiency, he found that the normal-soil ecotype showed no growth on serpentine soil even when this was supplemented by NPK treatments, which greatly benefited the serpentine ecotype growing on serpentine soil.

BIOTIC ECOTYPES   Biotic ecotypes have been selected by response to some biological feature of the environment. The most common biotic selection pressure is that of animal grazing. In areas of grassland subjected to particularly high grazing pressure (for example, around a drinking hole in a game reserve), grasses and other herbaceous plants with a normally upright habit will be selected for those ecotypes that are prostrate and thus less liable to have their vegetation and reproductive portions removed.

As grazing and browsing pressures are universal in all vegetation, many ecotypes with protective devices may long since have become dominant over unprotected ecotypes. Nevertheless, the unprotected form may sometimes be located and raised artificially, as was the thornless blackberry, for example. Ecotypes with protective devices are therefore, like prostrate ecotypes, a form of biotic ecotype.

Speciation

Through mutation and introgression followed by selection, modification of gene frequencies, and recombination, the great majority of species populations come to be composed of a number of freely interbreeding biotypes, or races, each adapted to a particular combination of parameters in the habitat. Such a species is known as a *polytypic species*. When the component populations of a polytypic species are readily distinguishable by morphological characters, they are frequently called *subspecies*. This term is especially applied to geographical races of animal species. In plants, as already discussed, races of a species that have distinct habitat requirements are commonly described as *ecotypes*. Species are said to be *polymorphic* when the characters that distinguish biotypes within them are qualitative and discontinuous rather than quantitative and continuous.

From time to time a mutation occurs in a segment of a polytypic species, such as an ecotype or a subspecies, that limits its ability to exchange genes with other segments of the parent species. The population that develops from the mutant is *reproductively isolated* and is commonly recognized as a separate species population, distinct from the original species. Before further mutation completely restricts all gene exchange between the parent population and the new one, there may be for one reason or another some further crossing between them, which is known as *hybridization*. Hybrids frequently fail because of the weakness of their phenotypes or through failure to reproduce normally. In plants the doubling of the chromosome content of hybrid individuals sometimes overcomes this sterility, a phenomenon known as *polyploidy*.

Populations that occupy different geographical areas are said to be *allopatric,* whereas those that occupy the same area are said to be *sympatric*. Although it is not implicit in the meaning of these two terms, they are now usually applied only to related populations; allopatric populations are defined as segments of an original population that have become separated by *spatial isolation*. Although members of the spatially isolated segments still interbreed with the original population where they are contiguous, the segments tend to become reproductively isolated also by a process known as *genetic drift*.

The Hardy-Weinberg law requires that an allele not subject to selection pressure remain at a constant frequency in a population. This frequency, however, will be an *average* frequency; that is, it will fluctuate about a mean figure in successive generations purely by chance. This fortuitous fluctuation in allele frequency may be directional. When it is so, it is called *genetic drift,* first named by Sewall Wright. In a large population genetic drift will have little or no effect, as fluctuation about the mean frequency will average out. In a small population, however, chance variation in the frequency of an allele may result in its extinction or its *fixation,* that is, its being represented in the homozygous condition in all individuals.

The extreme values for gene frequency—that is, zero per cent and 100 per cent—are commonly the ultimate fate of alleles in small populations. Before this final result, however, the gene frequencies in small isolated segments of a population may attain values very different from those of the parent population. In these small populations, therefore, genetic drift is a major factor in evolution and thus in speciation.

Table 3-3. Mechanisms That Bring About Reproductive Isolation of Species Populations

Prezygotic mechanisms—These prevent fertilization and zygote formation.
  Habitat—Populations live in same regions but occupy different habitats.
  Seasonal or temporal—Populations exist in same regions, but are sexually mature at different times.
  Ethological—Populations are isolated by different and incompatible courtship behavior.
  Mechanical—Cross-pollination is prevented or restricted by differences in reproductive structures.
Postzygotic mechanisms—Fertilization occurs and hybrid zygotes are formed, but these are inviable or give weak or sterile hybrids.
  Hybrid inviability or weakness.
  Development of hybrid sterility—Hybrids are sterile because gonads develop abnormality or because meiosis breaks down before it is completed.
  Segregational hybrid sterility—Hybrids are sterile because of abnormal segregation in gametes of whole chromosomes, chromosome segments, or combinations of genes.
  F_2 *Breakdown*—F_1 hybrids are normal, vigorous, and fertile, but the F_2 contains many weak or sterile individuals.

Largely modified from G. L. Stebbins, *Processes of Organic Evolution* (Englewood Cliffs, N.J.: Prentice-Hall, Inc., 1966), p. 97.

Speciation may be considered to have occurred when two populations can exist sympatrically, that is, in the same area. The ability of two populations to exist sympatrically without losing their identity through hybridization is regarded as a test of their reproductive isolation; to the extent that they do so, species populations are characterized by such isolation. The principal mechanisms that bring this about are listed in Table 3-3. Prezygotic mechanisms either prevent contact between species populations when they are reproductively active or restrict the union of gametes after mating or cross-pollination has occurred. Postzygotic mechanisms prevent the fertility or variability of the F_2 hybrids.

Prezygotic Mechanisms

In animals the chief prezygotic mechanism producing reproductive isolation is *ethological isolation*. The elaborate courtship displays of animals have a dual function. First, they overcome the mechanisms that maintain the individual distance, but second, they provide recognition signals for potential mates from the same species population. The conspicuous plumage and elaborate songs of many male birds are obvious examples of courtship displays, but even the inconspicuous fruit fly *Drosophila* has been shown to have highly complex and specific courtship patterns. These render a female susceptible to copulation with males of her own species, but not with males of different but very closely related *Drosophila* species. It has been shown experimentally that the wrong type of courtship display fails to remove inhibitions in the female. This ethological isolation can be overcome by anesthetization of the female or detachment of its antennae; in either case the inhibition no longer operates, and males from different species can copulate with the female.

In plants a frequent prezygotic mechanism that prevents crossing between sympatric species populations is differences in reproductive time. Because such seasonal differences can vary greatly from year to year, this by itself is not a completely effective isolating mechanism, and it is commonly encountered in combination with some other. Among higher plants the most effective such mechanism is difference in flower structure. By limiting the type of pollinator that can obtain nectar, these differences dictate a different range of pollinators, thereby restricting species populations to visits from pollinators that will not visit other species populations.

Postzygotic Mechanisms

Postzygotic mechanisms generally lead to a weak or inviable F_1 hybrid, a viable but sterile hybrid, or a viable fertile hybrid that produces a weak or inviable F_2. Sterility in hybrids is usually due to the failure of meiosis in gamete formation or to structural difference between the parental chromosomes. The production of weak or inviable offspring is generally attributed to what is called *genetic disharmony*. This phenomenon is not yet well understood, but it may be associated with DNA replication and the formation of messenger RNA.

Ecological Niches

Related species populations, whether of animals or of plants, are thus normally separated from one another not by one but by several isolating mechanisms. This, plus the fact that these isolating mechanisms are produced by several chromosomal or genic differences, suggests that species populations are not created at a single step but result from the accumulation of a number of different genetic changes. However, geneticists now place less emphasis than formerly on these genetic isolating mechanisms.

The various species populations that occupy an undisturbed habitat have usually evolved over a long period of time by changes in gene frequency controlled by natural selection until, in terms of population dynamics and gene frequency, they have reached equilibrium. Each population in the habitat can then be defined by a series of biological characteristics and physical parameters, and this set of characteristics and parameters that describe each species is known as its ecological niche, as will be discussed in the next chapter. It is now considered that it is the niche differentiation that occurs as a response to selection pressures that is the major determining factor in speciation, rather than genetical isolation by one means or another.

It will be seen in Chapter 4 how formulation of the Lotka-Volterra equations and the initial studies of Gause on competition between two species of yeast, followed by other experiments such as those of Park with flour beetles, have led to the conclusion that only one species population with a particular set of biological characteristics and responses to chemical and physical parameters can occupy one habitat. This conclusion emphasizes the uniqueness of each ecological niche; it is epitomized in what is usually known as the *competitive exclusion principle*. According to this principle, only one species population can have the same set of biological characteristics and responses to physical parameters, and so be associated with the one particular ecological niche, and vice versa.

It must be emphasized that the ecological niche is a functional characteristic of a biological population, not a physical location. Until a habitat is occupied by at least one species population, it does not contain any ecological niches. A recently created habitat, such as a volcanic island, is sometimes said to have unoccupied niches. This is using the term *niche* in the different sense of a *spatial niche*. The intention of the phrase is to express the fact that it takes time for the biological characteristics of the pioneer populations that arrive on the island to diversify sufficiently to reach a new evolutionary equilibrium with the environmental parameters of the habitat.

Species Diversity

The number of ecological niches in a given habitat is a function not only of evolution but also of habitat productivity. Until there has been sufficient time for the selection of populations completely adjusted to the full range of environmental conditions in the habitat, the gene frequencies of individual species populations will not have reached equilibrium. The number of individual gene pools, that is to say, the number of species populations ultimately developing, will be determined partly by the productivity of the habitat. The number of ecological niches that evolve in a given habitat is one expression of what has come to be known as its *species diversity*. Because the number of niches that develop is also a function of productivity, species diversity is a measure of the productivity of a habitat, although it must be noted that Paine has shown that polluted areas may have a low species diversity but a high productivity. Species diversity is one of the unique characteristics of a community; it has been extensively treated in the companion volume in this series by R. H. Whittaker.

Island faunas have been used by E. O. Wilson and R. H. MacArthur to demonstrate the development of species diversity, or expansion of the number of ecological niches. When an island has few species on it, most of the chance arrivals there belong to species not yet represented and the immigration curve at first is high, falling away later as the chance of individuals of different species' arriving become progressively less. At the same time, the more the species that arrive on the island, the more that can become extinct, so that the extinction curve rises as the immigrant curve falls. Finally the extinction curve intersects the immigration curve; at this point the rate of extinction just balances the rate of immigration. The island has now reached an equilibrium as to species diversity and therefore has developed the maximum number of ecological niches. Further speciation on the island can occur only if there is an equivalent amount of extinction, or evolution of new species proceeds.

Because the primary production of food depends on the initial amount of energy entered into the system, the productivity of a particular habitat tends to increase from the polar regions toward the Equator. This is so because the radiant energy supplied in each region varies from a minimum at the poles to a maximum at the Equator. As discussed in the companion volume in this series on community ecology, the complete explanation of variation in species diversity is actually much more complicated than this; its poleward decrease is only one aspect of the matter. Thus species diversity, being a function of productivity and evolution, also increases from the polar regions to the Equator. To illustrate this latitudinal phenomenon, MacArthur and Connell list the number of birds that breed in a range of political areas of varying but not entirely uncomparable size (Table 3-4). Despite variations in size between the various regions listed in Table 3-4, tiny tropical Panama has three times the number of bird species of huge subarctic Alaska.

Table 3-4. Number of Bird Species Breeding in Regions from the Arctic Circle to the Equator

Alaska	222
British Columbia	276
Washington	235
Oregon	232
California	286
Mexico	764
Guatemala	472
Nicaragua	477
Costa Rica	603
Panama	667

From R. H. MacArthur and J. H. Connell, *The Biology of Populations* (New York: John Wiley & Sons, Inc., 1966), p. 182.

Table 3-5. General Increase in Species Diversity with Decreasing Latitude in North America

	Florida	Massachusetts	Labrador	Baffin Island
Beetles	4,000	2,000	169	90
Land snails	250	100	25	0
Mollusks (tidal zone)	425	175	60	—*
Reptiles	107	21	5	0
Amphibians	50	21	17	0
Freshwater fish	—	75	20	1
Coastal marine fish	650	225	75	—*
Flowering plants	2,500	1,650	390	218
Ferns and club mosses	—*	70	31	11

* No data.

After G. L. Clarke, *Elements of Ecology* (New York: John Wiley & Sons, Inc., 1954), p. 488.

There are some exceptions to this general rule that species diversity increases in a gradient from the polar regions to the Equator, but most groups of plants as well as animals show similar behavior. Table 3-5 illustrates this general increase in species diversity with decreasing latitude in North America.

The term *species diversity* is used to express the number of populations present in a particular habitat. For convenience these populations are called species populations, but their precise taxonomic nature is very variable. Some of the animal populations would be perhaps better regarded as subspecies; some of the plant populations, as ecotypes. The only criterion by which the populations can be separated is their genome, for each population will represent a distinct gene pool, which while retaining its separate identity may still engage in gene exchange with neighboring populations.

Species diversity as so envisaged takes no account of *species abundance,* that is, the number of individuals in each population. This is sometimes expressed as a *diversity index,* the ratio of the number of species to the number of individuals in a given community or habitat. Abundance of plants in a community is commonly expressed in a frequency diagram (Figure 3-4). In such a frequency diagram, it is usually apparent that a few species are abundant, many are rare, and a varying number are of intermediate occurrence.

Niche Changes

As already described, the term *ecological niche* covers an abstract concept embracing the biological, chemical, and physical parameters of a particular population in a given habitat. A modification of the biological,

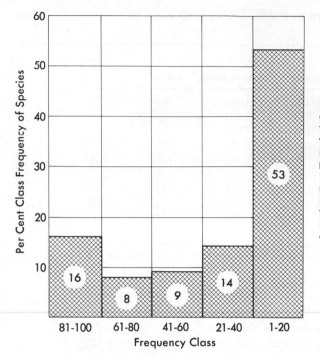

Figure 3-4. Frequency diagram. A histogram showing the frequency of occurrence of individuals of particular plant species in five frequency classes. The pattern illustrated is the normal Raunkiaer frequency of occurrence of many plant populations in homogeneous stands; when their frequencies are grouped into five classes, a double peak occurs.

chemical, or physical factors must correspondingly modify both the population and the niche. In the discussion of the predator-prey relationship in Chapter 4 it is noted that natural selection would tend to operate in two mutually contradictory directions: predators would be selected for a greater capture ability, prey for a greater escape capacity.

In the example of the peppered moths in industrial Britain, the occurrence of melanistic forms as a result of selection pressure illustrates well the selective modification of gene frequencies, with a consequent niche and habitat shift. In these moths, as described by Kettlewell, the melanistic gene was dominant. Its persistence in the population before industrialization, despite an apparent negative selection, was supposedly due to the fact that darker moths are more difficult to detect *on the wing* than lighter ones. There would therefore be some selection pressure for the dominant gene, as well as the larger one for the recessive pale condition. The case illustrates how a mutant may be maintained in a population at a low gene frequency by one selection pressure, then with an environmental change can be raised to a much higher frequency by a different selection pressure.

A more general niche modification resulting from environmental change occurs during the colonization of a newly created island. The best-known example of this was first described by Charles Darwin from observations he made during the voyage of H.M.S. *Beagle* to the Galapagos Islands in the early nineteenth century. These islands are of volcanic origin, generally believed to have been formed over a million years ago and never to have had any physical connection with the South American mainland. All the populations now found on the islands are believed to have been transported in one way or another over the six hundred miles of water that separate the islands from the mainland.

Darwin was especially interested in the Galapagos finches, of which he found some thirteen species populations. On the mainland, finches form a closely related group of insectivorous birds. On the Galapagos there were three main genera recognizable, in which the species of ground finches, tree finches, and warbler finches were placed. One of the tree-finch species had a parrotlike beak and was basically a vegetarian. Another, the woodpecker finch, climbed trees in search of insects in the cracks of bark, extracting them by means of a cactus spine that it carried in its otherwise too short beak. Of the ground finches, three species had become seedeaters; a fourth had a sharp beak and fed on prickly pear. In fact, in the comparative absence of competition on the Galapagos Islands, the finches had radiated to develop a number of ecological niches that on the mainland are formed by entirely different birds.

Such a process is known as *adaptive radiation*. In geological time, each major plant and animal group that has appeared has, by adaptive radiation, come to develop ecological niches in many habitats. The extent to which natural selection has effectively furthered adaptive radiation has determined the persistence or elimination of the populations involved and of their ecological niches. In some instances only a few populations from a vast range of adaptive radiation survive from a past age. Such is the case with the crocodiles and caymans and other alligators from the rich dinosaur reptilian fauna, and with coniferous species from the assemblage of Coal Age gymnosperms.

Occasionally groups have been preserved that well represent the adaptive radiation of a previous biological age and permit comparison with contemporary radiation. The marsupial fauna of Australia is an outstanding example of this. The adaptive-radiation process and formation of ecological niches of the marsupials, whose young are nourished mostly externally through the mammae, can be contrasted with those of the placental mammals, among which the gestation period is much longer and the embryo requires nourishment through a special organ, the placenta. Among the marsupials of Australia are a mole, a wolf, and a mouse; a flying phalanger, which resembles a flying squirrel; the wallaby, which is similar to a jack rabbit; the wildcat, which resembles a native cat; the wombat, which is the marsupial version of the anteater; and other forms. The Australian marsupials, which now number some 175 species, have had at least some 70 million years to achieve this adaptive radiation. Supposedly their ecological viability as dominants in Australian habitats is adequate, but in other parts of the world where the ancestral marsupials were in direct competition with eutherian mammals and were predated by them, this ecological viability was not sufficient to secure their survival as dominants.

Ecological Equivalents

Similar biological, chemical, and physical characteristics of separate habitats will impose the development in them of much the same form of ecological niche, whatever biological group happens to be available. Thus the evolution of grasslands presented the opportunity for the evolution of a grazing-animal niche throughout the subtropical world, which was achieved by the bison in North America, wildebeest in Africa, and the kangaroo in Australia.

Such niches are developed by what is known as ecological equivalents. The niches of the Australian marsupials and of placental mammals are ecological equivalents. Most cases, however, involve only pairs of species, not a whole continental fauna. A plant example may be found in the rapidly growing tropical-rain-forest pioneer tree species. In the New World, these are formed from the genus *Cecropia;* in the Old World, species of *Musanga* have a similar niche. The giant lobelias and senecios of high altitudes on the East African mountains have developed an ecological niche similar to that of physiognomically equivalent forms on the Andes, which are of quite different taxonomic classification.

References and Further Readings

BOUGHEY, A. S. "Ecological Studies of Tropical Coast Lines." *Journal of Ecology,* 45:665–687 (1954).

CAMIN, J. H., and P. R. EHRLICH. "Natural Selection in Water Snakes (*Natrix sipedon* L.) on Islands in Lake Erie." *Evolution,* 12:504–511 (1958).

CLAUSEN, J., and W. M. HIESEY. "Experimental Studies on the Nature of Species IV. Genetic Structure of Ecological Races." *Carnegie Institute Washington Publication,* No. 615, 1958.

CODY, M. L. "A General Theory of Clutch Size." *Evolution,* 20:174–184 (1965).

DUNBAR, M. J. "The Evolution of Stability in Marine Environments." *American Naturalist,* 94:129–136 (1960).

EHRLICH, P. R., and P. H. RAVEN. "Differentiation of Populations." *Science,* 165:1228–1232 (1969).

GREGOR, J. W. "Some Reflections on Intraspecific Ecological Variation and Its Classification." *Transactions of the Botanical Society of Edinburgh,* 34:377–383 (1946).

HALDANE, J. B. S. "The Cost of Natural Selection." *Journal of Genetics,* 55:511–524 (1957).

HAMILTON, T. H. *Process and Pattern in Evolution.* New York: The Macmillan Company, 1967.

HARPER, J. L. "A Darwinian Approach to Plant Ecology." *Journal of Ecology,* 55:247–270 (1967).

JOHNSTON, R. F., and R. K. SELANDER. "House Sparrows: Rapid Evolution of Races in North America." *Science*, 144:548–550 (1964).

KETTLEWELL, H. B. D. "The Phenomenon of Industrial Melanism in Lepidoptera." *Annual Review of Entomology*, 6:245–262 (1961).

KING, J. L. "Continuously Distributed Factors Affecting Fitness." *Genetics*, 55:483–492 (1967).

KRUCKEBERG, A. R. "The Ecology of Serpentine Soils. III. Plant Species in Relation to Serpentine Soils." *Ecology*, 35:267–274 (1954).

LACK, D. "Evolutionary Ecology." *Journal of Animal Ecology*, 34:223–231 (1965).

———. "Tit Niches in Two Worlds." *American Naturalist*, 103:43–49 (1969).

LEDLEY, R. S., and F. H. RUDDLE. "Chromosome Analysis by Computer." *Scientific American*, 214(4):40–46 (1966).

LEOPOLD, A. S. "Adaptability of Animals to Habitat Change." In *Future Environments of North America*, F. F. Darling and J. P. Milton (eds.) New York: Doubleday & Co., Inc., 1966.

LEVINS, R. *Evolution in Changing Environments*. Princeton, N.J.: Princeton University Press, 1968.

McMILLAN, C. "Ecotypes and Community Function." *American Naturalist*, 94:246–255 (1960).

MAYR, E. "Isolation as an Evolutionary Factor." *Proceedings of the American Philosophical Society*, 103:221–230 (1959).

MOONEY, H. A., and W. D. BILLINGS. "Comparative Physiological Ecology of Arctic and Alpine Populations of *Oxyria digyna*." *Ecological Monographs*, 31:1–29 (1961).

SOKAL, R. R., and P. H. A. SNEATH. "Efficiency in Taxonomy." *Taxonomy*, 15:1–21 (1966).

STEBBINS, G. L. *Processes of Organic Evolution*, 2nd ed. Englewood Cliffs, N.J.: Prentice-Hall, Inc., 1971.

TURESSON, G. "The Selective Effect of Climate upon the Plant Species." *Hereditas*, 14:99–152 (1930).

VAN VALEN, L. "Morphological Variation and Width of Ecological Niche." *American Naturalist*, 99:377–390 (1965).

WALLACE, B., and A. M. SRB. *Adaptation*, 2nd ed. Englewood Cliffs, N.J.: Prentice-Hall, Inc., 1964.

WHITE, M. J. D. "Models of Speciation." *Science*, 159:1065–1070 (1968).

WOOD, A. E. "Eocene Radiation and Phylogeny of the Rodents." *Evolution*, 13:354–361 (1959).

Chapter 4 • Population Interactions

The effects of the physical or abiotic environment on populations were considered in the last two chapters, dealing respectively with the proximate and ultimate results. The first chapter explored the primary characteristics of populations including growth and reproduction, density regulation, equilibrium, fluctuation, and periodicity. These phenomena represent the special field of study of the population ecologist, just as the proximate effects of chemical and physical environmental factors are the domain of the physiological ecologist. However, population phenomena are not restricted to these two proximate areas, or to the ultimate evolutionary features discussed in the previous chapter. Populations do not exist as isolated entities relating only to their physical environment, but interact extensively and continuously with one another. The purpose of this chapter is to investigate the nature of this biotic interaction.

Competition

In the opening chapter one particular aspect of biotic interaction in living systems was considered, *intraspecific competition*. It was seen how interaction between *individuals* in a population produces density-dependent interactions that lead to the logistic growth of a population. This intraspecific and density-dependent competition is expressed by Equation 1-6 on page 5:

$$\frac{dN}{dt} = rN\frac{(K - N)}{K}$$

which simplifies to

$$\frac{dN}{dt} = rN - \frac{rN^2}{K}$$

The effect of *interspecific* competition can be represented mathematically, starting from a basis of this expression of logistic growth. If, instead of one species population, two were introduced simultaneously into the same culture solution, the rate of population growth of one species would be modified by the extent to which the second species utilized the same resources, in this case the nutrients of the culture medium. The interaction that arises between two or more species populations in such a situation is known as *competition*. The nature of competition between species populations under cultural conditions has been very clearly described by L. B. Slobodkin; his models will be presented here. They have been further developed by Wilson and Bossert (1971).

When two species populations N_1 and N_2 are simultaneously introduced into a culture medium, the rates of population increase will be r_1 and r_2, respectively; the carrying capacities, perhaps better described in this instance as the saturation values, will be K_1 and K_2.

The effect of this density-dependent relationship on population growth may be expressed in the case of the first population by our saying that the inhibiting effect of one individual on its own population growth is $1/K_1$. Its inhibitory effect on the other species can be written as β/K_2, β being the competition coefficient of the second population. Conversely, the effect of one individual of N_2 on the growth of species population N_1 is α/K_1, α being the competition coefficient of the first population. Population growth in each of these two populations may thus be represented by

$$\frac{dN_1}{dt} = r_1 N_1 \frac{K_1 - N_1 - \alpha N_2}{K_1}$$

$$\frac{dN_2}{dt} = r_2 N_2 \frac{K_2 - N_2 - \beta N_1}{K_2}$$

Equilibrium will be established when

$$\frac{dN_1}{dt} = \frac{dN_2}{dt} = 0$$

All values of N_1 when $dN_1/dN_2 = 0$ must lie on the line $N_1 = K_1 - \alpha N_2$. Plotted as a graph with N_1 as the horizontal coordinate and N_2 as the vertical coordinate, the N_1 intercept will be K_1, and the N_2 will be K_1/α. Correspondingly, N_2 will have an N_2 intercept of K_2 and an N_1 of K_2/β. All possible combinations of N_1 and N_2 will cross the N_1 zero isocline vertically and the N_2 isocline horizontally.

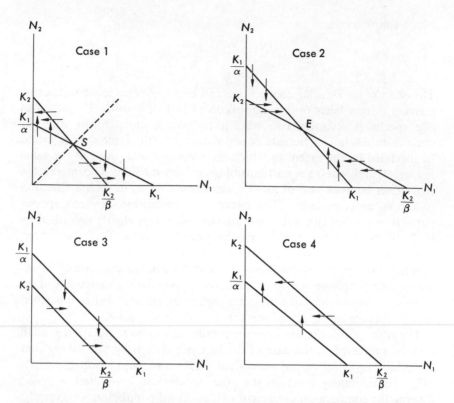

Figure 4-1. Interaction between pairs of species. In each case the lines K_1 to K_1/α and K_2 to K_2/β represent the saturation values for species N_1 and N_2, respectively. As indicated by the short arrows, neither species can increase above its saturation line. Below its saturation line, each species will increase. There are four cases. Case 1: Unstable equilibrium is possible at point S, but it is to be expected that one and only one species will survive. Which species survives depends on whether the initial mixture of species lies to the right or left of the line OS. Case 2: Stable equilibrium occurs at point E. Initial concentrations of the two species are irrelevant. Case 3: Species N_1 will always win in competition because the region between K_1/α to K_1 and K_2 to K_2/β is below the saturation level of N_1 but above the saturation level of N_2. Case 4: Species N_2 will always win in competition because the region between K_1 to K_1/α and K_2 to K_2/β is below the saturation level of N_2 but above the saturation level of N_1. From *Growth and Regulation of Animal Populations* by Lawrence B. Slobodkin, p. 64. Copyright © 1961 by Holt, Rinehart and Winston, Inc. Reprinted by permission of Holt, Rinehart and Winston, Inc.

Competition between two species populations in a nonreplenished culture therefore offers four possible results (Figure 4-1).

1. Either N_1 or N_2 will alone survive, depending on the initial concentration, when

$$\alpha > \frac{K_1}{K_2} \quad \text{and} \quad \beta > \frac{K_2}{K_1}$$

2. The two species coexist when

$$\alpha < \frac{K_1}{K_2} \quad \text{and} \quad \beta < \frac{K_2}{K_1}$$

3. N_1 is the sole survivor when

$$\alpha < \frac{K_1}{K_2} \quad \text{and} \quad \beta > \frac{K_2}{K_1}$$

4. N_2 is the sole survivor when

$$\alpha > \frac{K_1}{K_2} \quad \text{and} \quad \beta < \frac{K_2}{K_1}$$

From these models, Slobodkin proceeds to consider the concept of the ecological niche which was extensively treated in the previous chapter of this text.

An actual species population, as opposed to the hypothetical ones postulated in Slobodkin's models, must have a distribution in both *space* and *time*. It will occupy a given area for a specific period. The environmental parameters in which the species is included must lie within the tolerance limits of the species population. It was seen in Chapter 2 that where these parameters are, for example, temperature and moisture, a two-dimensional figure known as a climograph can be constructed. The temperature and moisture environment of the species population is then definable as the space included in this climograph.

Approximately ten years ago G. E. Hutchinson developed from such a basis as this the idea of a *multidimensional volume,* representing the totality of environmental parameters defining the conditions under which a species population could exist and reproduce. This volume he called the *fundamental niche* of the population, attributing the term to MacArthur.

The term *niche* has been applied in a variety of ways in ecology. Odum defines an ecological niche as the status of an organism within its habitat that results from its adaptation, physiological responses, and behavior; here and in the previous chapter the concept defined is a *functional niche.* On the other hand, the concept of a *spatial niche* is sometimes used to indicate some location in a habitat where a species may occur. Further consideration will be given later to these several niche concepts.

Gause's Competition Experiments

One conclusion from the development of the above models is that it is impossible for two species populations to continue to occupy the same ecological niche. This can be determined from equations proposed independently by A. J. Lotka and V. Volterra over forty years ago now known as the *Lotka-Volterra equations*. Another major conclusion is that although chemical and physical factors defining an ecological niche normally vary continuously, the result of competition between species populations in the same culture or area will be *discontinuous distribution*.

The former conclusion was first confirmed experimentally by the Russian biologist G. F. Gause and is sometimes known as *Gause's hypothesis*. This term is now, however, regarded as less satisfactory than the phrase *competitive exclusion principle*, introduced by G. Hardin.

In these now-classic studies, Gause utilized two species of yeast, which were grown both separately and together in a culture medium. This medium was not renewed in any of the cultures, so that growth ceased before all the sugar was exhausted, supposedly when alcohol accumulation in the culture medium became toxic to the yeast. Two yeast species populations were introduced simultaneously into equal volumes of culture medium, and the competition coefficients α and β were calculated from the following equations.

$$\alpha = \frac{K_1 - \dfrac{dN_1/dt \times K_1}{r_1 N_1} - N_1}{N_2}$$

$$\beta = \frac{K_2 - \dfrac{dN_2/dt \times K_2}{r_2 N_2} - N_2}{N_1}$$

Gause obtained the following values for the competition coefficients of the two yeasts.

First Yeast	Second Yeast
$\alpha = 3.15$	$\beta = 0.439$

Thus one unit volume of the first yeast decreased the unutilized opportunity for growth of the second yeast 3.15 times more than one unit volume of the second yeast would. Assuming that it is alcohol that limits the population growth of these cultured yeasts, the competition coefficients can also be evaluated in terms of the relative rates of alcohol production. Differences between the competition coefficients calculated in these two ways caused Gause to conclude that either one yeast produces something in addition to alcohol that affects the growth of the other or one yeast is affected in its growth not only by alcohol but also by some other metabolite.

When the experiments were repeated with aerated cultures, the population data coincided completely with the relative rates of alcohol production. Gause therefore concluded that some respiratory by-product, presumably carbon dioxide, was involved in the anaerobic interaction but did not modify it under aerated conditions.

Gause subsequently performed similar experiments using species of *Paramecium*. Recently it has been concluded that some of Gause's experiments are open to other interpretations, but the real significance of his work remains unaffected. He provided an empirical description of population growth under particular circumstances that confirmed experimentally the Lotka-Volterra theoretical equations. He could also identify physiological factors affecting the growth of populations.

Other Experiments

The nature of competition between related species populations under laboratory conditions has been further investigated by T. Park in a long series of experiments. In some of these, Park used two closely related species of flour beetle, *Tribolium confusum* and *T. castaneum*. Starting with mixed populations under a range of slightly varying cultural conditions, he found that one or the other species eventually was eliminated; only one species survived. It appeared from these experiments that particular combinations of moisture and temperature condition the balance between competing flour-beetle populations (Table 4-1).

As in the case of Gause the interpretation of some of the experiments has subsequently been challenged, but their basic ecological conclusions remain valid.

Exploitation and Interference

Consideration of such experiments as those on flour beetles just described caused T. Park to separate competitive interactions between populations into two components, *exploitation* and *interference*. *Exploita-*

Table 4-1. Competition Between Two Species Populations of Flour Beetles

Climate	Temperature (°C)	Relative Humidity (per cent)	Percentage of Replicate Experiments in Which Only One Species Survived	
			Tribolium castaneum	*Tribolium confusum*
Hot-wet	34	70	100	0
Hot-dry	34	30	10	90
Warm-wet	29	70	86	14
Warm-dry	29	30	13	87
Cool-wet	24	70	31	69
Cool-dry	24	30	0	100

Data from T. Park, *Physiological Zoology*, 27(3):177–238 (1954).

tion develops when two species are competing for the same resource. This is usually food or space. *Interference* occurs when two species are not competing in this exploitation sense, but when their coexistence in the same habitat modifies some behavioral pattern of one or the other. For example the mere sight or smell of a male mouse of a different species may cause recently fertilized females of some species to abort.

When both exploitation and interference develop between sympatric species, competition is most intense. It is convenient to separate these two elements, but biologists have not made extensive use of this distinction.

Competition Under Natural Conditions

Competition under natural conditions is more difficult to investigate quantitatively than competition under controlled laboratory conditions. Connell, in a well-known study on barnacles of the genera *Balanus* and *Chthamalus,* has been able to demonstrate that the zonation relationships are due to interspecific competition. Barnacles, once attached, live the rest of their lives and die in the same spot; it is therefore very simple to record the distribution of individuals in barnacle populations. In Scotland, where the work was done, individuals of the *Balanus* species population occur lower down on rocks in the intertidal zone than those of the *Chthamalus* population. Although young individuals of *Chthamalus* were frequently established in the lower zone also, they did not grow there as rapidly as did the young of *Balanus;* the upper zone was not colonized by *Balanus* at all. The young *Chthamalus* individuals in the lower zone were therefore either overgrown or pried off the rocks in the lower zone by the more vigorously expanding *Balanus.* If *Chthamalus* was not in contact with *Balanus,* it could live in the lower barnacle zone, from which it was demonstrably excluded under natural conditions by interspecific competition (Figure 4-2).

As has been described by Harper and his associates, somewhat similar experiments with plant populations produce much the same results as those with flour beetles. In an experiment in which mixed populations of a number of barley varieties were sown in different habitats, there was a tendency for the mixtures to be reduced after a number of years to a population of one variety, varying in identity with the location.

Harper and his co-workers have demonstrated that competition between plant species is in some instances a competition for soil microsites suitable for seed germination. The varied microenvironments offered by a soil surface act selectively on mixed seed populations, determining the numbers of safe germination sites. In many of the experimental populations examined, the number of individual plants established was a direct function of the number of safe microsites on the soil surface. It was concluded that in these experiments slight differences in seed shape and surface, interacting with subtle variations in the structure of the soil

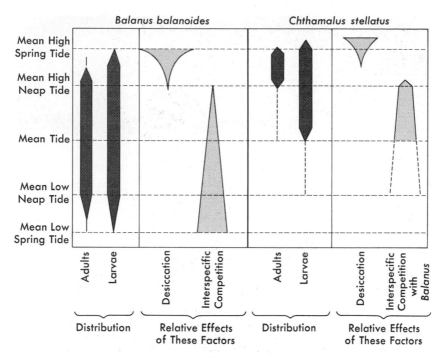

Figure 4-2. Competition between two barnacle species populations in an intertidal gradient. Individuals of *Chthamalus* are established throughout the inter- tidal zone, but they are subsequently overgrown or pried off by the faster-growing *Balanus* in areas where physical factors do not limit the occurrence of individuals of the *Balanus* population. Redrawn from J. H. Connell, *Ecology,* 42:710–723 (1961).

surface, possibly influenced both the abundance of particular plant species and the balance between the species.

Allelochemistry

One further aspect of competition under natural conditions has recently come under more extensive investigation. It relates to the interference aspects and develops from the biotic release of toxic chemical substances into the environment, more especially by plants. These *allelochemicals,* as they are called, which are sometimes referred to as *secondary plant substances,* may suppress growth in the same or other populations (Figure 4-3). Their effect was first demonstrated in California chaparral by C. H. Muller, and the extensive literature that has already appeared on this topic was recently reviewed by Whittaker and Feeney.

The earliest allelochemicals to gain recognition were the antibiotics, of which penicillin is both the first and the most famous example. Muller demonstrated the interference effects of terpenes, which are volatile aromatic substances occurring in plants, especially in species of the

Figure 4-3. Competition between species through allelochemical influences.
Bare soil surrounding a patch of *Salvia leucophylla* in chaparral in Southern California.
The ring of bare soil results from the suppression of germination and the growth of
various grasses and forbs, owing to the release of terpenes from the *Salvia* shoots.
These gaseous aromatic allelopathic substances are adsorbed by the surrounding soil.

Figure 4-4. Pioneer plants on a fire burn. When chaparral in Southern California
burns, there is frequently a subsequent massive growth of pioneer species, as here.
Many of these pioneer species germinate from seeds previously present in the soil
but held dormant by allelopathic substances, such as terpenes or phenols. These are
temporarily dispersed by the passage of the fire.

Lamiaceae. Later he showed that water-soluble phenols in plant tissues had rather similar interference effects. In fact the well-described resurgence of vegetation on old fire burns in chaparral is a result of the previous allelochemical suppression of seeds dormant in soil. Fires temporarily diminish these allelopathic effects and permit a large-scale germination of these seeds (Figure 4-4).

Apart from these plant/plant interference types of competitive inter-actions, and rather similar animal/animal ones, allelochemical substances are of extreme significance in plant/animal predation interactions. Were it not for the general and widespread occurrence of such allelochemical substances in plants, they would long since have been totally consumed by insect and mammalian herbivores.

Selective Effects of Competition

The selective effects of competition, whether for resources in a given habitat or for sites within it, will have a marked effect on the extent of variation that is maintained in species populations. The effect will be related to the taxonomic nature of the competing populations. If the habitat is occupied by a species population composed of potentially interbreeding but geographically or ecologically discrete segments, such as subspecies or ecotypes, competition between these environmentally determined segments will tend to extend variation within the individual populations until it approximates to the variation within the habitat. Gene flow will still occur between these segments, but particular com-binations of gene frequencies will be selected under the stress of com-petition for particular sets of environmental conditions. That is to say, competition will tend to widen the biological variation already present in the segments (Figure 4-5 **C**).

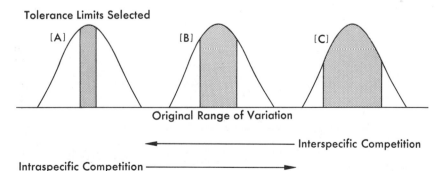

Figure 4-5. The range of variation under different breeding systems. **B** repre-sents the tolerance limits for an ecological factor, such as temperature, for a species population. **A** represents the situation when the species population is exposed to competition from closely related species; there is selection for narrower tolerance limits. **C** represents the situation when the population has broken down into competing segments, such as subspecies; the over-all tolerance range of the species widens.

If, on the other hand, the habitat is occupied by competing independent species populations, gene flow will accordingly be very much more restricted. The pressure of interspecific competition will in this case select from each species population those genomes that confer a special adaptation to a particular and limited range of the environment. Competition in this instance will tend to narrow the biological variation occurring within each of the competing species (Figure 4-5 A).

Character Displacement

When two populations with overlapping tolerance limits for the same environmental character compete, each will have its original range of variation modified, as illustrated diagrammatically in Figure 4-6. Selection will ensure that the amount of overlap between the new tolerance limits is minimal, because it will minimize the deleterious effects of competition. Thus similar species sympatric in only a portion of their range will be modified solely in this portion, not in their allopatric areas.

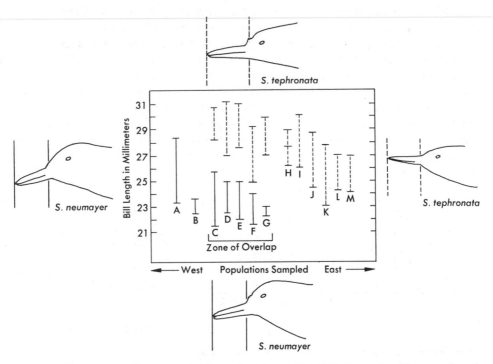

Figure 4-6. Character displacement in a pair of bird species. Two species of nuthatch occur in the Middle East and the East, *Sitta neumayer* and *S. tephronata*. Where the species are sympatric, their bill length, and other features such as the position of the facial stripe tend to be different, whereas they are quite similar in allopatric areas. Redrawn from C. Vaurie, *Proceedings of the International Ornithological Congress, 1950,* pp. 163–166 (1951).

This phenomenon, which occurs extensively in partially sympatric species, is known as *character displacement*. It was first described in terms of variation in bill length and head coloration of two species of Asiatic nuthatch. The first especially is important, for it strongly influences the nature of the food taken. Sometimes in omnivorous species the displacement may separate the similar species into two distinct trophic levels. It is then known as *trophic displacement*.

Cohabitation

Experiments such as those of Park and Gause demonstrate that two noninterbreeding populations cannot occupy the same habitat if they are in direct and precisely overlapping competition for some resource of that habitat, and the Lotka-Volterra models show that such populations cannot exist together in equilibrium if they share a controlling factor. However, under natural conditions, species populations may frequently be observed occupying the same habitat in apparent defiance of these experiments and theoretical conclusions. Thus visitors to a Southern African game reserve should not be overly optimistic in hoping to encounter lion, leopard, and cheetah in the same day's run. All three of these predator species may coexist within the same habitat; the lion may feed largely on buffalo or wildebeeste, the leopard on baboons and monkeys, and the cheetah on young kudus or waterbuck, and other lesser animals from small antelope to guinea fowls.

This is a rather obvious example of the utilization of different food resources of the habitat by coexisting species, a phenomenon commonly described as *niche diversification*. The avoidance of competition may be achieved by differential utilization of habitat resources other than food (Figure 4-7), and further and more subtle differences have been observed. The work of Harper has demonstrated that different plants require generally differing microhabitats for their seed germination and establishment. Another form of behavior affording the possibility of cohabitation is the utilization of the same resource at a difference season or time of day. Diurnal squirrels utilize much the same food in the same habitat as nocturnal pack rats. In the African tropics, scarab beetles live on elephant and buffalo dung in the summer, whereas in winter this resource is monopolized by termites. A forest in the northeastern United States will support vernal populations such as herbaceous species of *Trillium* and *Cornus*—which complete the most productive portion of their annual life cycle in direct spring light—before the summer canopy of the dominant deciduous trees has developed and reduced the amount of radiant energy available to them.

These examples of cohabitation illustrate the phenomenon of *coexistence,* a general occurrence under natural conditions.

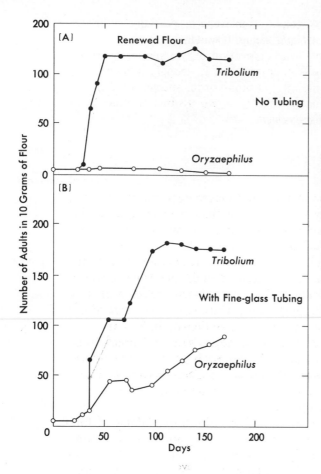

Figure 4-7. Niche diversification permits cohabitation. A: *Tribolium* outcompetes *Oryzaephilus* in cultures of populations of the two beetles maintained in renewed flour. B: Where fine-glass tubing has been added to the medium, niche diversification has permitted cohabitation of the same culture by both beetle populations. After A. C. Crombie, *Proceedings of the Royal Society, Series B*, 133:88, 94 (1946).

Coexistence

The vast majority of populations have reached an equilibrium in their particular habitat. This being so, they must then exhibit two fundamental characteristics. First, they have some method of population regulation; second, because, under natural conditions, no populations exist in isolation as pure cultures, they have some means of coexistence with other populations in the same habitat with which they interact. Coexistence can take a variety of forms, examples of which are the alternating utilization of food or energy that have already been mentioned. The nature of the interaction between two coexisting populations has been defined by Slobodkin as falling into one of five types:

1. The two populations may compete for some of the resources of the habitat.
2. The second population may serve as a resource for the first.
3. The first population may serve as a resource for the second.

4. The two populations may be of mutual benefit.

5. The two populations may be quite independent.

The first situation has already been examined. It is known as *inter-specific competition* and produces further niche diversification. The second and third call for one population to serve as a predator and the other as a prey.

Predation

Predation is an example of interaction between two species populations that, like competition for food, can produce a negative rate of increase r in one of the two interacting populations, and may threaten its survival. Under natural conditions, the effect on r tends to be smaller when the interacting populations have had a long evolutionary history in a particular habitat. Natural selection appears to reduce or even eliminate the detrimental effects on r of the interaction. This is not entirely surprising when it is realized that the continuing depletion of a prey by a predator would ultimately and inevitably lead to the extinction of the prey and therefore of both populations. The most severe predator-prey interactions are more usually observed between populations only recently or temporarily associated. The emergence of man as the most excessively destructive animal yet evolved has produced many changes in populations that through his intervention have recently or temporarily been caused to interact.

The effect of human disturbance on an existing predator-prey equilibrium may be equally dramatic. One frequently cited example of this is the spectacular fluctuation in population density of the Kaibab deer. The Kaibab Plateau in Arizona, an area of approximately 727,000 acres, is estimated to have carried some 4,000 deer at the beginning of this century. From 1907 to 1917, 600 mountain lions were removed; from 1918 to 1923, 74 more were removed; and from 1924 to 1939, 142 more. From 1907 to 1923, 3,000 coyotes were taken and from 1923 to 1939, 4,388 more were taken. From 1907 to 1923, 11 wolves were killed, and this predator was considered exterminated by 1939.

The removal of these predators caused spectacular increases in the deer population (Figure 4-8). By 1924 they had risen in number to 100,000. In the two winters of 1924–1925 and 1925–1926, there were population crashes in which 60 per cent of the population died from starvation and disease. Still further losses occurred, and in 1939 there were about 10,000 deer surviving on a depleted range, whose carrying capacity was probably originally about 30,000 animals.

Natural selection acts in completely opposite, mutually contradictory directions on the predator-prey interaction; characters of the prey will be selected that increase its ability to avoid being eaten. The predator will evolve more efficient mechanisms for catching and eating its prey.

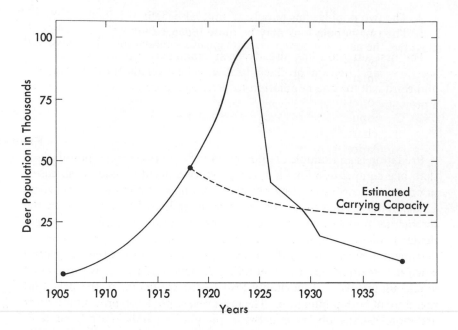

Figure 4-8. Population explosion in Kaibab deer following removal of predators. A population of about 4,000 deer in 1906 increased rapidly following the drastic reduction in the numbers of mountain lions, coyotes, and wolves, all of which had preyed on the deer. The increase in deer numbers overshot the estimated carrying capacity (dotted line), and the inevitable crash occurred. Redrawn after Leopold from W. C. Allee, et al., *Principles of Animal Ecology* (Philadelphia: W. B. Saunders Company, 1949), p. 706.

Moreover, one population of prey may be utilized by more than one predator population. This can lead to a situation such as occurs among insects, where there may be more predatory species than herbivorous ones among a particular taxonomic group. The interaction between predator and prey is therefore complex and is not yet fully understood.

However, two comparatively recent developments have provided some assistance in advancing our conceptualization of predation. The first is a series of experiments undertaken by C. S. Holling and his associates; the second is an extension of the Lotka-Volterra model, expounded by Wilson and Bossert. Most recently there has been one further change, initiated by the work of David Janzen, and that is to employ the word *predation* to all of Slobodkin's class 2 and 3 relationships. This is a logical procedure, but it necessitates regarding *herbivory* or the consumption of living organic material by plant-eating animals as predation, as well as *carnivory*, which has always been so regarded. This matter is considered further in Chapter 6.

Holling undertook a series of laboratory experiments designed to elucidate the nature of predatory interspecific interactions. These involved predation by deer mice on saw fly cocoons. He started from the premise that these interspecific effects would relate to the following variables:

1. The population density of the prey.
2. The population density of the predator.
3. Prey characteristics in relation to predator avoidance.
4. Population density of other prey, or relative abundance of other predator food resources.
5. Predator characteristics in relation to prey capture.

Under his laboratory conditions, Holling could eliminate points 4 and 5 as unknown variables, and control variable 2. The nature of the prey eliminated variable 3. Holling could then in his experiments investigate the effect of prey density variable 1 on predator density variable 2. His experiments, later confirmed by field investigations, demonstrated that over one section of the range, the rate of predation is prey density-dependent. However at low prey population densities, prey mortality is reduced and predation may no longer be density-dependent. The prey population may then increase again until density-dependent factors again exercise an overriding influence on predation. Obviously variable 4, *prey-switching*, which Holling did not investigate in this series of experiments, is of great importance. Its significance is considered further in Chapter 6.

Wilson and Bossert have noted that the Lotka-Volterra equations are too simple, generating errors in regard to the levels of population densities at which a predator/prey equilibrium is achieved. They have without rewriting the original equations proposed a modification of the graphical form of the theory by making two changes in the prey zero-growth curve. These changes and their implications are illustrated in Figures 4-9, 4-10, and 4-11.

Regarding predation in more practical terms as a general factor contributing in some measure to population density regulation, there seems to be broad agreement with the *compensating predation* theory of P. L. Errington. This may be summarized as stating that the maximum population density which can be maintained through the most inclement season of the year represents the carrying capacity of the habitat for a given species. When birth rates have provided numbers in excess of this, surplus animals are easily predated, or die from starvation, disease, or some other cause. Should the consequent losses from one cause or another

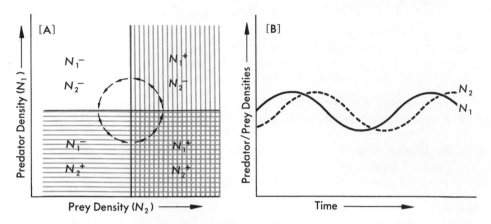

Figure 4-9. Theoretical predator-prey interactions. Various authorities, such as R. H. MacArthur, M. Rosenzweig, J. H. Connell, E. O. Wilson, and W. H. Bossert have developed theoretical models to explain fluctuations in predator-prey populations on a basis of the Lotka-Volterra equations. In this diagram, the prey population density increases below the median horizontal line (prey zero growth line) in **A**, and falls above it. The predator population *decreases* to the left of the median vertical line (predator zero growth line), and *increases* to the right of it. If the joint directions in which the combined predator-prey populations are moving at any moment of time are represented by an arrow, any disturbance of this system will cause this arrow to travel in a circular counterclockwise path, as indicated.

Plotting this path as in **B** as a function of time shows regular oscillations in predator (N_1) and prey (N_2) populations. Close parallels to this theoretical type of predator-prey population cycle may occur in natural situations, as shown in Figure 4-8. However, this model is generally too simple to represent most field cycles; it is further developed in the next two figures.

bring the population density far below the carrying capacity, the subsequent reproduction rate will be higher than usual. That is, predation can be regarded as a density-dependent factor, removing especially the young and the old, as well as other unfit animals.

Parasitism

In predation one population, the predator, utilizes as a resource a second population, the prey; individuals of both populations have an independent existence until the moment of the act of predation. When the resource relationship between two populations is more intimate and individuals of the population utilizing the other as food actually locate themselves in or on individuals of the other population, the interaction is called *parasitism*. Individuals of the one population occur as *ectoparasites* upon or as *endoparasites* within individuals of the second species, which is known as the *host*.

The relationship between parasite and host populations is essentially similar to that between predator and prey. However, many parasite

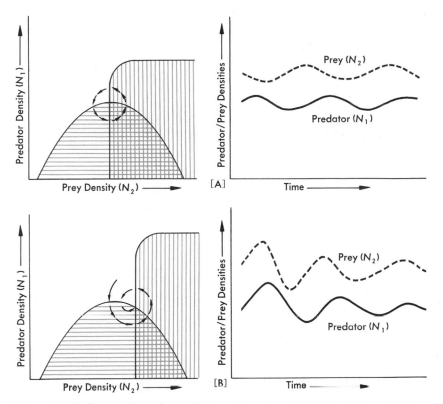

Figure 4-10. Fluctuations in predator and prey populations. When predator-prey populations are spatially restricted, the predator can eat the prey faster than it can reproduce, and both populations may then move toward extinction; therefore, it is better to represent the prey zero population line of Figure 4-9 by a curve, as here. In the situation in.**A**, the prey zero population curve and predator zero population line still intersect at right angles, as in Figure 4-9: the resulting cycle is still a stable one and likewise quite rare under natural conditions. In **B**, the prey zero growth curve is mostly beyond the predator zero growth line. The joint directions of the combined populations will tend to spiral inward, showing a damping effect on oscillations in the two populations. Redrawn from MacArthur and Connell, 1966, and other authors.

populations can utilize individuals of the same host population, whereas in general only one or a few predator individuals can utilize one prey individual. One large mammal, such as an elephant, or one tree generally entertains a considerable variety of ectoparasitic and endoparasitic populations.

Parasite-host relationships occur far more extensively, and have been much more commonly investigated, than predator-prey relationships because of their economic significance in agriculture, forestry, and horticulture, and their major importance in human pathology. Wilson and Bossert direct attention to a deduction from the original Lotka-Volterra equations known as *Volterra's principle,* which is particularly relevant in

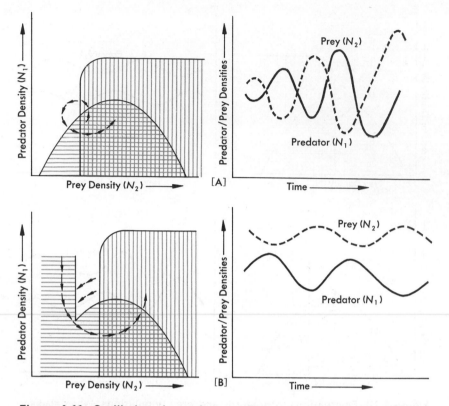

Figure 4-11. Oscillations in predator and prey populations. This continued development of the model in Figure 4-10 illustrates theoretically what occurs when the prey zero curve mostly lies inside the predator zero line **(A)**. In this case the joint population directions spiral *outward:* this situation is highly unstable and leads ultimately to the extinction of both populations. Many simple laboratory predator-prey systems show this kind of cycle. If, however, the prey is provided with a refugium in which predation may be avoided, as in **B,** the cycle becomes a stable one without any further change. This is a very common natural situation. The predator feeds especially on the surplus prey individuals, which are not able for one reason or another to avail themselves of the protection of the refugium. Redrawn from MacArthur and Connell, 1966, and other authors.

this context. This principle notes that both the natality of a predator and the mortality of its prey are determined by the product of the predator and prey population densities. Thus if some environmental change reduces these densities by an equal proportion, the effect will be greater in the product than in the individual densities. That is, a spray treatment killing 95 per cent of an insect pest and 95 per cent of a parasite upon it will alter in the pest's favor the relative natality of the parasite and the relative mortality of the pest. Hence spraying for pest control that produces an incomplete kill may permit a pest, temporarily at least, to escape from regulation by its predators and parasites.

Symbiosis

The physical association of individuals of two populations does not evoke inevitably a predator/prey or parasite/host relationship. There appears to be a series of degrees of interdependence, running the whole gamut of relationship from Slobodkin's types 2 and 3 through type 4 to type 5, that is, from predation or parasitism through mutual inter-dependence to complete independence. To demarcate and classify such relationships, a series of terms have been employed, such as *commensalism, mutualism, amensalism, protocooperation,* and *neutralism.* E. P. Odum has attempted to express this range of relationships in tabular form (Table 4-2); his system is in effect an extension of Slobodkin's definition of types of interaction. All such interspecific interactions when they stop short of

Table 4-2. Analysis of Species-Population Interactions

Type of Interaction	Effect of Relationship on Growth and Survival of Two Populations				General Result of Interaction
	When Not Interacting		When Interacting		
	A	B	A	B	
Neutralism (A and B independent)	0	0	0	0	Neither population affects the other.
Competition (A and B competitors)	0	0	−	−	Population most affected eliminated from niche.
Mutualism (A and B partners, or symbionts)	−	−	+	+	Interaction obligatory to both.
Protocooperation (A and B cooperators)	0	0	+	+	Interaction favorable but not obligatory to both.
Commensalism (A, commensal; B, host)	−	0	+	0	Obligatory for A; B not affected.
Amensalism (A, amensal; B, inhibitor in allelopathy, or antibiotic in antibiosis)	0	0	−	0	A inhibited; B not affected.
Parasitism (A, parasite; B, host)	−	0	+	−	Obligatory for A; B inhibited.
Predation (A, predator; B, prey)	−	0	+	−	Obligatory for A; B inhibited.

After E. P. Odum, *Fundamentals of Ecology,* 2nd ed. (Philadelphia: W. B. Saunders Co., 1959), p. 226.

an actual predatory relationship may be considered examples of *symbiosis.*

The word *symbiosis* was originally used for relationships such as that believed to exist between the algal and fungal components of a lichen. The alga was thought to supply carbohydrates to the fungus and to receive from it inorganic and organic nitrogen compounds. The relationship between nitrogen-fixing bacteria of the genus *Rhizobium* and their leguminous hosts, later shown to exist between other nitrogen-fixing organisms and hosts from other taxonomic groups, was also considered symbiotic in this classical sense. The term is now used for any interaction between two populations that would appear to confer some additional selective value either to the individual population components or to their relationship. Its application also to the parasite-host and predator-prey relationships is generally regarded as too forced.

Other Mutualistic Interactions

Mutualism, as defined to include both the classical interpretation and the broader modern concept of symbiosis, is of extremely wide occurrence. Space permits only the most meager reference here to a few examples of it. Perhaps because of the long and relatively stable periods of evolutionary history that ocean systems have enjoyed, some of the most complex and most spectacular examples of mutualism have been described from marine habitats. One such remarkable example is provided by the cleaner wrasse (*Labroides phthirophagus*). These fish, which are obligate cleaners, remove material from the mouths of larger fish whose teeth thereby supposedly have a diminished exposure to dental caries. Larger fish will wait patiently at a "cleaner station" for their turn to be "cleaned." Other small fish mimic the cleaner fish and similarly escape being eaten while scavenging in the mouths of the larger fish. Another example of mutualism is provided by the highly colored clown fish (*Amphiprion percula*), which swim freely within the tentacles of tropical sea anemones without becoming paralyzed by their stings (Figure 4-12). In this instance it is conjectured that the fish enjoy a greater measure of security from competition, and even from predation, in their sanctuary, while the anemones scavenge any food morsels inadvertently dropped by the fish.

Equally spectacular, on occasion, and certainly extremely numerous terrestrial examples of mutualism are to be found in pollination biology and diaspore dispersal mechanisms. These have been known and extensively described for a long time, although their real significance was often not understood until it was more recently exposed by such workers as L. Van der Pijl and H. G. Baker. A less widespread but equally interesting mutualistic relationship has been described by David Janzen in the genus *Acacia,* and now found in other common genera such as Cecropia. A sedentary prey species, such as a plant, is obviously very restricted in the

Figure 4-12. Mutualism. Increasing numbers of mutualistic interactions are now being described; many have long been known in marine ecosystems. One of the more spectacular of these occurs between the clown fish and certain tropical sea anemones in which they shelter. As shown here, the fish are apparently immune in this sanctuary to the paralyzing stings that would immobilize any other animal of this size. It is conjectured that the anemones may scavenge morsels of food inadvertently dropped by the fish.

range of predator avoidance mechanisms it may adopt. A plant group such as that represented by the many species of *Acacia* may adopt one or more of three main strategies for the avoidance of this predation, which would otherwise be so heavy as to cause extinction. If a plant contains toxic substances, or resembles a species that does, it will be avoided, as has already been discussed when describing allelochemicals on p. 89. If its shoots are armed—that is, have developed hooks, spines, stings, or other protective devices—few animals will be able to predate it. Or it can develop a mutualistic relationship with a "protector" species. Janzen has shown that some Central American forest *Acacia* species have done just that. Their thorns house ant colonies that sally out and attack any animal attempting to predate their host tree. At the same time the host produces certain tissue "buds" that appear to have no function other than to provide food for the ant colonies. There are many such similar mutualistic interpretations that could be described that have developed between our own species and domesticated animals and plants.

References and Further Readings

BAKER, H. G., and P. D. HURD. "Intrafloral Ecology." *Annual Review of Entomology,* 13:385–414 (1968).

BROOKS, J. L. and S. I. DOBSON. "Predation Body Size and Composition of Plankton." *Science*, 150:28–35 (1965).

BROWER, L. P. "Ecological Chemistry." *Scientific American*, 220(2):22–29 (1969).

BROWN, W. L., L. T. EISNER, and R. H. WHITTAKER. "Allomes and Kairomones: Transpecific Chemical Messengers." *Bioscience*, 20:21–22 (1970).

BROWN, W. L., and E. O. WILSON. "Character Displacement." *Systematic Zoology*, 5:49–64 (1956).

CONNELL, J. H. "The Influence of Interspecific Competition and Other Factors in the Distribution of the Barnacle *Chthamalus stellatus*." *Ecology*, 42:710–723 (1961).

DARWIN, J. H., and R. M. WILLIAMS. "The Effect of Time of Hunting on the Size of a Rabbit Population." *New Zealand Journal of Science*, 7:341–352 (1964).

ERHLICH, P. R., and P. H. RAVEN. "Butterflies and Plants." *Scientific American*, 216(6):104–113 (1967).

ERRINGTON, P. L. "The Phenomenon of Predation." *American Scientist*, 51:54–68 (1968).

FAEGRI, K., and L. VAN DER PIJL. *The Principles of Pollination Ecology*. Toronto-London: Pergamon Press, Inc., 1966.

GRIFFITH, K. J., and C. S. HOLLING. "A Competition Submodel for Parasites and Predators." *Canadian Entomologist*, 101:785–818 (1969).

HARDIN, G. "The Competitive Exclusion Principle." *Science*, 131:1292–1297 (1960).

HARPER, J. L., and J. N. CHATWORTHY. "The Evolution and Ecology of Closely Related Species Living in the Same Area." *Evolution*, 15:209–227 (1961).

HOLLING, C. S. "The Functional Responses of Predators to Prey Density and Its Role in Mimicry and Population Regulation." *Memoirs of the Entomological Society of Canada*, 45:5–60 (1965).

HORNOCKER, M. G. "An Analysis of Mountain Lion Predation upon Mule Deer and Elk in the Idaho Primitive Area." *Wildlife Monograph No. 21*, Washington, D.C.: The Wildlife Society, 1970.

JANZEN, D. H. "Coevolution of Mutualism Between Ants and Acacias in Central America." *Evolution*, 20:24–75 (1966).

———. "Seed-eaters Versus Seed Size, Number, Toxicity and Dispersal." *Evolution*, 23:1–27 (1969).

LAMB, J. M. "Lichens." *Scientific American*, 201(4):144–156 (1959).

LIMBAUGH, C. "Cleaning Symbiosis." *Scientific American*, 205(2):42–50 (1961).

MACARTHUR, R. H., and R. LEVINS. "The Limiting Similarity, Convergence, and Divergence of Co-existing Species." *American Naturalist*, 101:377–385 (1967).

MULLER, C. H. "Allelopathy as a Factor in Ecological Process." *Vegetatio*, 18:348–357 (1969).

PARK, T. "Experimental Studies of Interspecific Competition. II. Temperature, Humidity and Competition in Two Species of *Tribolium*." *Physiological Zoology*, 27:177–238 (1954).

PIMLOTT, D. H. "Wolf Predation and Ungulate Populations." *American Zoologist*, 7:267–278 (1967).

RASMUSSEN, D. L. "Biotic Communities of Kaibab Plateau, Arizona," *Ecological Monographs*, 11(3): 229–275 (1941).

SCOTT, G. D. *Plant Symbiosis*. London: Edward Arnold & Co., 1969.

SLOBODKIN, L. B. "How to Be a Predator." *American Zoologist*, 8:43–51 (1968).

TAKAHASHI, F. "Functional Response to Host Density in a Parasite Wasp, with Reference to Population Regulation." *Researches on Population Ecology,* 10:54–68 (1968).

VAN DER PIJL, L. *Principles of Dispersal in Higher Plants.* Berlin: Springer-Verlag, 1969.

WENT, F. W., and N. STARK. "Mycorrhiza." *BioScience,* 18:1035–1039 (1968).

WHITTAKER, R. H., and P. R. FEENEY. "Allelochemics: Chemical Interactions Between Species." *Science,* 171:757–770 (1971).

WILSON, E. O., and W. H. BOSSERT. *A Primer of Population Biology.* Stamford, Conn.: Sinauer Associates, Inc., 1971.

Chapter 5 • The Behavior of Populations

So far in this text we have considered the intrinsic nature of populations and the essential characteristics that they exhibit, such as growth and adaptation. We have examined the nature of the environmental interactions that modify these features, developing a multiplicity of feedback regulatory mechanisms, noting that these may also in their turn have the reverse effect of modifying the environment. One last vital feature of populations remains to be considered, that is their *behavior*.

The ecological study of behavior had generally been neglected until the last two decades, especially at the population as opposed to the individual level. Indeed an Animal Behavior Society was not founded until 1964. There were several reasons for this, one of the main causes being that American psychobiologists concentrated especially upon the memory and learning aspects of behavior. It was mostly left to their European counterparts to investigate the area of *ethology,* the behavior of populations as observed in natural ecosystems. Greater emphasis on ethological studies in this country is currently developing, partly as a result of improvements in electronic telemetering devices. Another modern innovation is the extensive availability of temporarily immobilizing drugs. The miniaturization of circuitry has made possible the remote tracking of adult tagged animals without serious disturbance either of individuals or of the population of which they are members. Behavioral features like migration and hibernation can thus be followed continuously in some species for the first time. Moreover, imminent threats to the continuing existence of many higher animals has necessitated detailed studies of such behavioral phenomena as habitat selection and adaptability to new environments. Finally, a growing interest in our own social organizations has stimulated investigations of the social behavior of various other animal populations, and particularly those of other primates.

Types of Behavior

It is possible, for convenience, to recognize three types of population behavior. The first, which can be called *accommodation,* relates to the position of a particular population within the habitats that it occupies. The second, *regulation,* refers to the social interactions within the population. The third relates to the *maintenance* of the population, that is, its reproductive behavior; this term has another established usage in the context of bird behavior.

These three types of behavior are exhibited by all population systems, whatever the nature of their individual members. Some populations will obviously be very limited in the extent to which they can display one or another of these characteristics because of the biological structure of the organisms involved. Terrestrial plants, for example, are for the most part severely restricted as to mobility. Their movements are generally confined to individual organs rather than to whole organisms. Microbial populations, whether located in an aquatic, aerial, or a terrestrial environment, by contrast may have extensive mobility, but generally of a passive kind. Movement of the first kind, which is restricted to a particular organ of a higher plant, is generally known as a *tropism;* that of the second kind, movement of an individual microscopic form, is usually categorized by the term *taxis* (Figure 5-1). Higher animals can be considered as exhibiting both these forms of movement, but they tend to be submerged in their much higher general mobility; the term *tropism,* in fact, is probably best

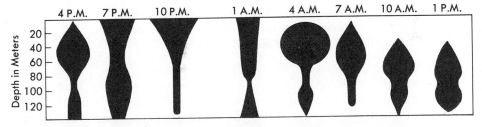

Figure 5-1. Tropisms and taxes. The so-called sleep movements of plants are commonly found in particular families of flowering plants. They relate in some cases to diurnal opening and closing of the leaves. Such tropisms may be induced by fluctuation in light intensity or relative humidity or in response to tactile stimuli. These limited movements of various organs are generally the maximum motor responses to irritability that rooted plants may display. By contrast free-floating microscopic plants, animals, and other microorganisms may react to these stimuli by limited movements or *taxes* of the whole organism, as shown here in the diurnal movement of zooplankton in a lake.

restricted to plant movement. *Behavior* is sometimes interpreted as a *capacity for mobility,* and its study may in a simplistic way be defined as observation of animal movement.

Accommodation

In terms of *accommodation* the behavior of higher animals has a very different time factor from that of attached plants. Because of this difference, natural selection for such features as habitat preferences or gregariousness takes on an equally different form. Among higher animals, populations may exhibit *social behavior.* Selection pressures in such a population, which increase clumping and thereby render a population much more "fit" than one in which the individuals are normally solitary, can operate to cause adaptation within one generation. Obviously sociality in plants has to be very different, and selection for it may take many generations. Moreover, in plants and microbes there is no tendency to select, for example, for the process that we term *learning.* By contrast, in a social population of higher animals, one in which its members acquire new knowledge from one another by social learning is very likely to be more "fit" than one in which they do not.

Social learning circumvents the necessity to rely upon the emergence of new genomes or further mutants to introduce new behavior in a population. Behavioral responses in social animals can be *learned.* Social learning confers upon the population the ability to adapt within one generation to particular environmental variations, rather than passing through several generations of selection before achieving the necessary adaptation. Of all the animal species, the one that has most outstandingly exploited this cultural learning aspect of behavior is our own. Social learning has enabled us, in effect, to escape from the confines of a single ecological niche, which still limits the ecological development of all nonprimate species. Social learning, even when not exploited to the extent it has been in our own species, nevertheless enables animal populations to achieve more readily what may be termed *adjustment.*

Adjustment

Populations may react or *adjust* to their environment in one of two ways. They can either undertake changes within their internal social organization, or they can remove themselves to a different environment. In both cases there is an essential preliminary need for sensory equipment to measure the environmental factors that are controlling and limiting the dispersal of the population and to which it must adjust. The response to the information obtained through this sensory equipment may be described as *irritability,* a term first applied to individual organisms.

Sensory Organs

All populations, whether of a plant, animal, or microbial nature, exhibit some form of irritability by virtue of the individual reactions of their members. The nature of this response may, however, be limited, as it is in the majority of rooted plants, which have not only limited irritability options, but also very restricted means of sensing changes in the environment to which they have the capacity to respond. Nevertheless, even this limited response may have considerable ecological significance. In the majority of animals there are sensory organs that respond to electromagnetic or other forms of wave motion conveying energy of the type that we call heat, light, or sound. Many animals have additional sensory organs responding to other environmental characteristics, such as tactile and, especially, chemical stimuli. All organisms appear to have some kind of response to gravity, although many apparently react to such features as water pressure, and some even to electric or magnetic fields.

Whatever the form of the environmental parameter that is sensed, the various sensory organs must relay the signal they receive to a point where it can be transmitted to a control center for interpretation, sorting, storage, and action decision.

Information-processing

In all higher animals control-center information-processing takes place in a specialized portion of the central nervous system known as the *brain*. We are just beginning to put together some understanding of the manner in which environmental signals are scanned and interpreted as patterns in the brain. It might be imagined that visual scanning by the eyes would transmit through the optic nerves a signal that would be interpreted into a pattern made available to the whole of the brain. That this is not so has only recently become clear from the study of individuals who have—congenitally, by accident, or by surgery—had the two hemispheres of the brain separated from one another. Although such studies as this may ultimately help to explain ecological adjustment, for the moment they are still handled by psychiatrists and psychobiologists.

Movement

In the more strictly ecological context, movement is thus especially a feature of animals, and it is one to which much of their sensory and information-processing equipment is devoted. Members of the majority of animal populations must possess mobility in order to *feed*, to *survive*, and to *reproduce*. By virtue of this mobility an animal can locate itself within a particular habitat and a given dispersal area for whichever of these purposes its innate mechanisms determine, as they interact with the environment. As noted earlier in this text, patterns of movement or behavior tend to be of a cyclic nature and are related to cyclic fluctuations in environmental parameters. The duration of daylight, especially, plays a conspicuous part as an environmental determiner in this respect. Through its effect on various control mechanisms—for example, on the pituitary gland of higher vertebrates—it controls the periodicity of their reproductive behavior. Likewise, operating through a differing mechanism, it exercises a major controlling influence on plants. In the case of animals, photoperiodic influences frequently change movement patterns radically; for higher plants this is not so for obvious reasons.

Increasing attention is now being given to the manner in which an animal locates itself within its habitat range for one or more of these essential purposes. Even from the earlier experiments, it became apparent that habitat location was strongly influenced by innate genetically determined characteristics. Much of this early work was performed on deermice. Harris, for example, working on two subspecies of the white-footed deermouse (*Peromyscus maniculatus*), showed that after members of these two subspecies were raised under laboratory conditions, they would, when offered the choice, select woodland or grass-land habitats according to the origin of their subspecies. This innately determined behavior was confirmed by Wecker in an elaborate series of experiments on the behavior of one of the same pair of subspecies of deermouse. Wecker constructed a long enclosure lying partly in woodland, partly in grassland. Deermice of the one subspecies that were raised in different ways were introduced to this enclosure, and their selection of habitat was automatically recorded. The deermice tested belonged to populations with six different histories. These were field-caught mice, their wood-raised offspring, their laboratory-raised offspring, laboratory-raised mice, their field-raised offspring, and their wood-raised offspring. Wecker observed that whatever their history, all animals bred originally from this one subspecies showed a preference for the grassland section of the enclosure. Despite individual early experience in a woodland habitat, there was no tendency for animals to prefer the woodland end of the enclosure, but the grassland-raised animals showed a reinforced preference for the field end of the enclosure (Figure 5-2).

Experiments such as these with deermice have been done on other animals with rather similar results. For example, Klopfer worked with adult chipping sparrows that had been raised without contact with either oak or pine foliage. Both of these occur in their natural habitat, but the sparrows are encountered mostly on pine trees. In Klopfer's experiment they showed a preference for the pine foliage when offered a choice.

These and all other such experiments tended to confirm that over a wide range of animals, the factors that determine habitat selection are basically innate, that is, genetically determined. It will be apparent that

Figure 5-2. Habitat selection in deermice. A semidiagrammatic representation of the enclosure built to determine the reaction of members of a subspecies of deermouse (*Peromyscus maniculatus*), obtained from various sources. Whatever the origin of the deme tested, its members invariably showed a preference for that portion of the enclosure that represented a field **(A)**, as opposed to a woodland habitat **(B)**. This was the closest simulation of the original habitat of the subspecies from which these various demes were originally derived. Drawn in simplified form from photographs in Wecker, 1963.

habitat selection characteristics cannot be rigidly determined; otherwise it would be impossible for a species to modify the requirements of its habitat without the occurrence of mutations. If habitat switches are to take place more frequently, there must be some degree of plasticity within the limits of the phenotypic variation of a particular generation of a given population. This plasticity is very strikingly illustrated by those animals that have moved into the urban ecosystems that we have created in the last fifteen thousand years. Indeed many species have done this so effectively that we now have considerable difficulty in dislodging pigeons, starlings, and rats, together with insects and arthropods of a number of kinds, from the urban habitats to which they have so rapidly adapted. Nor should we be so modest as to ignore our own simply fantastic plasticity in this respect. There are, however, some signs that we may now be pushing this plasticity to its limits, the thresholds for which can only be advanced in the future by a further genetic evolution of our species. The spacing experiments currently progressing, as described by P. R. Ehrlich in the paper cited at the end of this chapter, are especially interesting in this respect.

Feeding Behavior

As with habitat selection, the food-seeking behavior of a majority of animals appears also to be determined by innate behavioral patterns, reinforced in this instance by learned reactions. In many instances this behavior is quite stereotyped. The measure to which it must conform to a given pattern seems to be an expression of the degree of intelligence exhibited by the animal, when this is defined as the ability to associate independent stimuli. Feeding behavior must also contain a major energetics component, as shown by time and energy budgets such as those discussed by Wolf and Hainsworth.

The most frequently quoted example of the more stereotyped kind of behavior in an animal of low intelligence is provided by digger wasps. Adults of this species feed on the nectar of flowers and other naturally occurring sugary solutions. In order to provide for the nutrition of the young larvae, the gravid female becomes predatory and lays her eggs in a paralyzed prey. This is usually an arthropod of some kind, especially a cricket, grasshopper, cicada, or spider. Prey selection is triggered by a sequential series of stimuli. The predatory female first identifies her prey by visual selection. On closer approach this is supplemented by odor stimuli. If both the visual and the olfactory stimuli are sufficiently intense, a final tactile stimulus is necessary to invoke the stinging behavior that paralyses the prey. The methods by which the digger wasp transports the paralyzed prey, generally larger than herself, to her burrow or nest are equally stereotyped.

Although such a cause-and-effect pattern of behavior as this is more general among lower forms of intelligence, it does persist in other animals and especially in birds, which typically have a preponderance of innately determined behavior. Among herons and egrets, for example, the feeding behavior is so characteristic and distinct that it is possible to separate individual species taxonomically on a qualitative behavioral basis. This kind of niche differentiation by the assumption of different behavioral feeding patterns permits sympatry among a number of bird species that otherwise might encounter a high level of competitive exclusion.

Animal Navigation

Related to animal movement interactions in regard to habitat selection is the question of *animal navigation*. This is an extremely fascinating subject about which comparatively little is yet known. New instrumentation and the new tagging methods already referred to are making it possible to trace migratory movements more accurately (Figure 5-3), but the causal factors promoting migration, and the methods by which various populations orientate themselves during such mass or individual movements, remain largely unexplained.

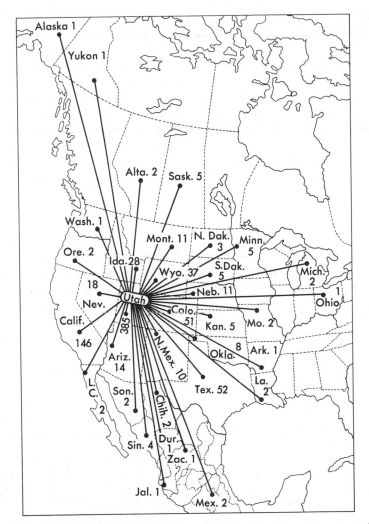

Figure 5-3. Radial emigration of ducks after the breeding season, as plotted from banded birds. After F. C. Lincoln, *Bird-Banding,* IV, 4:177–189 (1933).

The most distant annual migration known is that of the Arctic tern, which nests on the Arctic tundra in the northern summer and feeds in Antarctic waters during the southern summer. Many birds show seasonal but shorter annual migrations from their feeding to breeding grounds. So do some marine mammals like the fur seal and the gray whale. On land, caribou, for example, had until recent disturbances occurred an annual mass migration, so did the wildebeest in the African tropics. Most of these terrestrial migrations have now been stopped or foreshortened by the obstructions that human landscape development patterns have placed in their path.

Regulation

Having considered these various *accommodation* aspects of behavior, it is possible to proceed to consider *regulation*, the patterns of social interactions. Not only the adult feeding behavior, but also the mode of supplying food to the young, and the behavior of the young in receiving food, is generally equally stereotyped among birds, as well as in a considerable number of other animals. A very substantial amount of work has been done on these aspects in such species as the herring gull (Figure 5-4). Among mammals, initial stereotyped feeding behavior passes into learned behavioral patterns, which the juvenile stages gradually acquire and which relate to their own experience within their particular habitats.

Territoriality

One of the most interesting of these social behavioral patterns that develop in juveniles partly as the result of innate behavior patterns, partly as a result of learned reactions, is *territoriality*. This phenomenon is known to occur either continuously or seasonally among populations ranging from mammals through birds and fish to solitary and social insects and including some reptiles and amphibia. Aside from its significance in the regulation of population density, as discussed in Chapter 1, territoriality appears to have three main functions: the protection of a nest or den, the insurance of an adequate food supply, and a preempting of the space for a display area. The second function, when taken alone, defines not territory but a *home range* (Figure 5-5). This is the area over which the animal will range in search of food. It is not defended or marked, as is the case with the area of the territory as a whole (Figures 5-6 and 5-7).

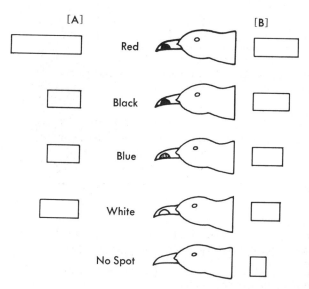

[A]   Red   Black   Blue   White   No Spot   [B]

Figure 5-4. Feeding responses in herring gulls. In an extensive series of experiments, Tinbergen and his fellow workers, using simulated herring gull heads of various shapes, sizes, and coloration, were able to demonstrate that the pecking response of the young gulls is directed most intensely toward a colored spot on an attenuated-shaped base of a different color. The size of the bars in experiment **A** and experiment **B** indicates the number of feeding responses invoked in individual chicks by a particular model. In **A** the beak portion of the model was uniformly colored as indicated; red produced the greatest response. In **B** of the variously colored (or no) spots on a yellow ground, the red spot had the largest response. Redrawn, based on Tinbergen, 1964.

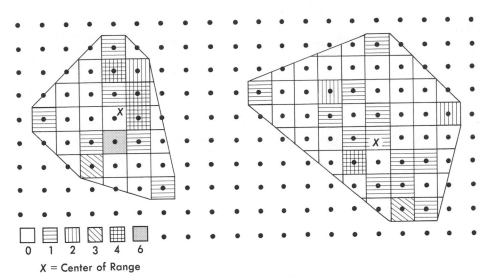

X = Center of Range

Figure 5-5. Home ranges of two breeding females of woodland deermouse (*Peromyscus maniculatus gracilis*) **in northern Michigan.** The large dots indicate traps spaced forty-five feet apart; the nest sites are located by the X's. The shading of quadrants indicates the number of times the animal was caught in each trap. From L. R. Dice, *Natural Communities* (Ann Arbor: The University of Michigan Press, 1952), p. 233.

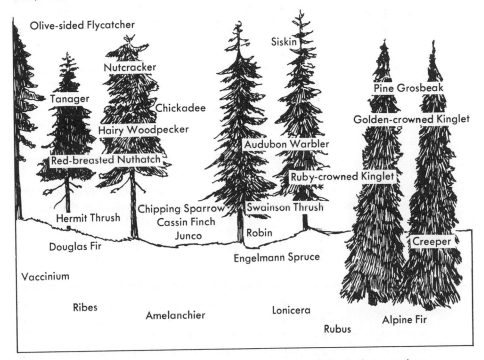

Figure 5-6. The vertical distribution of territories. Animals that use three-dimensional space, such as birds and insects, may have territories that are vertically layered. This familiar example illustrates such a vertical distribution of territories; it shows the most common location of a number of bird species in a spruce-fir forest in the northwestern United States. Compiled from various sources.

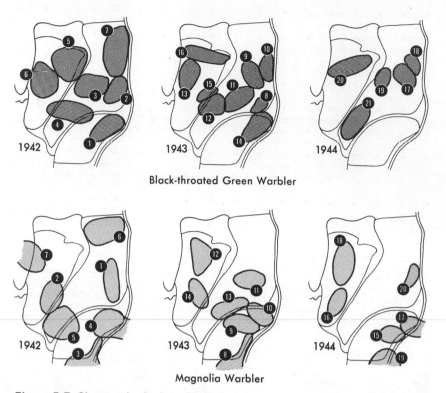

Black-throated Green Warbler

Magnolia Warbler

Figure 5-7. Changes in the locations of territories of two species of warblers in a beech-maple community in New York State over three successive years. From S. C. Kendeigh, *The Wilson Bulletin,* 57:145–164 (1945).

The marking of a territory may be achieved in a number of ways. Reference has already been made to bird song in this respect, but chemical methods of marking by *pheromones* are probably the most common. Pheromones are secreted by special glands; these may be located on the pads of animals, in which case as in many cat species, they scratch to mark territory, or they may mix with the urine or feces, as in dogs or rhinoceros, respectively.

Social Rank

Territory is one form of expression of spatial relationships between members of a population. In those animals that are gregarious rather than solitary, such relationships are controlled by *dominance hierarchies* or *social rank.* Again these have been most frequently explored in bird populations, although in this case they are a very general phenomenon of all social animals, whatever their systematic position. The first observations were made on flocks of domestic chickens, which were observed to have a "pecking order." In this the cockerels were usually in highest

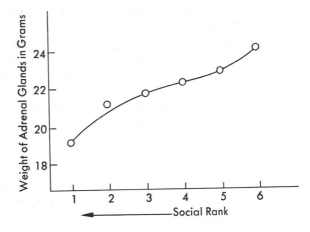

Figure 5-8. Correlation between social rank and the size of the adrenal glands. In the dominant male mice category (1) the size of the adrenal glands, expressed on a basis of milligrams per gram of body weight, was approximately the same as that of animals kept in isolation and thus protected from social stress. Subordinate ranks of mice (2–6) had glands that were successively larger with each progressive step down the social scale. Data extracted from D. E. Davis, *Integral Animal Behavior* (New York: The Macmillan Company, 1966).

order of dominance; the hens ranked below. If capons were included in the group, they assumed the lowest position. The injection of the male hormone, *testosterone*, into a capon, a cock, or a hen would advance the position of that individual in this social order (Figure 5-8).

Reproductive Behavioral Patterns

Social behavior such as territoriality or social ranking appears to have less influence on population mortality rates than it does on birth rates. Indeed many behavioral patterns appear to be designed to increase the occurrence of heterosexual encounters of individuals at appropriate stages. Clearly, for reproduction to occur the first problem to be solved is the recognition of another member of the same population; the second is the detection of a member of the opposite sex in the appropriate reproductive phase. The recognition of the first may be due at least in part to *imprinting*. The second is achieved by means of *courtship displays*.

Imprinting

During the first hours or days of independent existence in many higher vertebrates, the young learn to associate with any large moving object in their immediate surroundings. Usually this object will be the female parent. As reported by Hess, this type of learning was first observed in birds, but it has subsequently been recorded in a wide range of animals, especially in precocial forms. It is known as *imprinting* and is expressed as *following* behavior. That is the juveniles, when mobile, will follow the object with which they have learned to associate. As so brilliantly demonstrated by Konrad Lorenz, this object can be taxonomically quite unrelated. Ducklings will follow a hen, or even a man. Moreover, it operates in some ways in reverse, for a cat will brood chickens or a dog will nurse kittens.

This form of learning is believed to be impossible once fear develops, hence its transitory nature. However, the effects of imprinting are very much less impermanent. Through associations with appropriate visual, tactile, olfactory, or other stimuli, these effects probably assist as one determining factor enabling members of a particular population to recognize one another.

Courtship Displays

Once again, courtship displays have been very extensively studied in birds, although they occur in a wide range of animals, ranging from insects to mammals. Generally, they appear to be a behavioral device for overcoming individual conflict. In birds the method of expression of the courtship display is usually related to the nature of the environment that the animal most usually occupies. Raptors, such as eagles, most commonly have courtship displays taking the form of elaborate aerobatics. Diving birds may enlarge on their swimming performances. Birds that occupy more dense habitats, where visibility is limited, may develop displays based on elaborate songs or calls (Figure 5-9).

Parental Care and Social Learning

Courtship displays may continue to unite heterosexual individuals during the parental care stage of parenthood. Where the young have a considerable period of dependency upon the parents, the continuation of some behavioral pattern extending the association between the parents is clearly necessary. During this juvenile stage there is usually not only the feeding relationship, but also a considerable transmission of learned behavior from parent to offspring. This process of learning by *instrumental conditioning* may be conjectured to be a much less hazardous manner of acquiring the behavioral patterns necessary for survival than the simpler process of individual trial and error. It can be speculated that in species in which behavioral patterns are fairly complicated, not all juveniles are sufficiently intelligent or receptive to receive this social learning. Among predators it would appear that some of the young never acquire the necessary knowledge to enable them to hunt for themselves, and presumably they eventually perish.

Not only is learning transmitted from parents to offspring at this dependent stage, but the process of behavioral play enables juveniles to try out the patterns that are being communicated to them. Without this period of juvenile dependency, during which instrumental conditioning can be practiced in play periods, it would be difficult for learned behavioral patterns of a complicated form to be acquired and perfected.

Figure 5-9. Courtship displays in various species. These may assume very elaborate behavioral patterns, especially in birds, and involve one sex only or both sexes. **A:** Courtship ritual in the spined stickleback. **B:** Courtship signal in the fiddler crab; the male waves aloft a large and brightly colored claw. **C:** One of the courtship postures adopted by a prairie chicken cock. **D:** The commencement of a courting display in a mallard duck. **E:** Courtship display in a pair of herring gulls.

Primate Behavior

The last decade has witnessed a tremendous upsurge of definitive studies on comparative primate behavior. These studies have been concerned in particular with social groups and with such behavioral patterns as those related to what is described here as their *accommodation* like dispersal and habitat selection, their *regulation* such as feeding and watering, resting, sleeping, and play, and where applicable hibernation, prey selection, or predator avoidance, and their *maintenance*, that is, social organization and reproductive behavior.

The intricate nature of the relationship between females and their offspring has been extensively investigated by H. F. Harlow. He isolated newly born rhesus monkeys and provided them with access to different types of surrogate mothers. In a series of tests, one surrogate was a wire frame with a feeding bottle and a wooden face attached in appropriate positions. The other kind of surrogate in addition was covered with soft terry cloth. The young rhesus monkeys at first fed equally from either kind of surrogate, but as they aged, spent more and more time clinging to the material of the cloth-covered surrogates. Harlow and his associates also observed that rhesus monkeys reared in isolation on cloth-covered surrogates were incapable of normal adult social relationships. They could not defend themselves or establish any measure of social dominance and could not mate normally or establish the normal parental care patterns with their offspring.

P. C. Jay, working in the field on Indian langur monkeys, made observations on primate infant dependency that complement Harlow's laboratory experiments and conclusions. She observed an early infant relationship with its mother, as it rode about clutching her body. Then she recorded the gradual emancipation from maternal influence and the development of the essential peer relationships with other similarly aged offspring in the langur troop. Jay stressed that social behavior evolved as individuals matured, following a common series of behavioral pattern changes (Figure 5-10).

The conclusions of such behavioral studies have frequently been extrapolated by application to explanations of human social behavior. These rationalizations of human behavioral patterns and interpretations of hominid social evolution were enthusiastically adopted, sometimes without adequate regard to the applicability of these often specialized primate patterns to other species. Nevertheless some general conclusions appear to have been adequately substantiated by such experimental validification. Thus, in all primates there is a very close and intense relationship between female parent and offspring. This is indeed the most significant and the strongest bond that develops between primate individuals. By contrast with human societies, the male-parent-to-offspring bond in other primates is generally very weak. In a large number of cases the male parent is actually unknown and unrecognized.

With this close mother-to-infant bond, it is not surprising that the social ranking of a primate female tends to be transmitted to her offspring. In some baboon species, for example, where dominance is shared among several adult males, this inheritance of a social rank tends to create hereditary dominance cliques. Offspring of dominant females will have been less harassed during their infancy than the offspring of more lowly placed females; the males will tend to become members of the dominant clique. They will tend to inherit a high social rank merely by virtue of their habituation to a dominant position. This kind of situation it is tempting to regard as recurrent within human social patterns.

In more precise terms, information as to hominid behavior can sometimes be adduced from the study of living primates with comparable

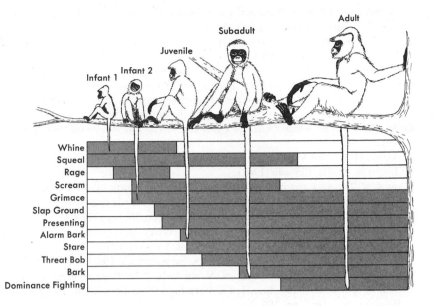

Figure 5-10. The development of social communication in langur monkeys.
In this primate species, which has been extensively observed by P. C. Jay, the methods
of social communication gradually extend, and become more sophisticated, as infants
progress through various juvenile stages to adulthood. Behavioral patterns, such as
social communication, show both this individual development and population evolution through time. From A. S. Boughey, *Man and the Environment* (New York: The
Macmillan Company, 1971), p. 38, adapted from P. C. Jay, 1965, with the permission
of the publisher.

morphology. Washburn has described instances of this applicability in
the interpretation of motor activities, such as walking and throwing, and
creative behavior, such as tool-making. Such critical studies are gradually
building up both a rational picture of the process of human evolution and
a more complete understanding of human behavior.

References and Further Readings

ALEXANDER, R. D. "Aggressiveness, Territoriality and Sexual Behavior in Field
    Crickets (Orthoptera: Cryllidae)." *Behavior,* 17:130–223 (1961).
CHRISTIAN, J. J. "Phenomena Associated with Population Density." *Proceedings
    of the National Academy of Sciences,* 47:428–449 (1961).
—— and D. E. DAVIS. "Endocrines, Behavior and Populations." *Science,* 146:
    1550–1560 (1964).
DELGADO, J. M. R. "Brain Research and Behavorial Activity." *Endeavour,* 26(99):
    149–154 (1967).
DETHIER, V. G. (ed.) *Topics in Animal Behavior.* New York: Harper & Row, Pub-
    lishers, 1971.

DE VORE, I. (ed.) *Primate Behavior: Field Studies of Monkeys and Apes.* New York: Holt, Rinehart and Winston, Inc., 1965.

EHRLICH, P. R., and J. FREEDMAN. "Population, Crowding and Human Behaviour." *New Scientist,* 50:10–14 (1971).

EVANS, H. E. "Predatory Wasps." *Scientific American,* 208(4):144–154 (1963).

GARTLAN, J. S., and C. K. BRAIN. "Ecology and Social Variability in *Cercopithecus aethiops* and *C. mitis.*" In *Primates: Studies in Adaptation and Variability,* P. C. Jay (ed.) New York: Holt, Rinehart and Winston, Inc., 1968, pp. 253–292.

GUHL, A. M. "The Social Order of Chickens." *Scientific American,* 194(2):42–46 (1956).

HARLOW, H. F., and M. K. HARLOW. "Social Deprivation in Monkeys." *Scientific American,* 207(5):136–146 (1962).

HARRIS, V. T. "An Experimental Study of Habitat Selection by Prairie and Forest Races of Deer-Mouse, *Peromyscus maniculatus.*" *Contributions from the Laboratory of Vertebrate Zoology,* University of Michigan, 56:1–53 (1952).

HARRISON, J. L. "The Distribution of Feeding Habits Among Animals in Tropical Rain Forests." *Journal of Animal Ecology,* 31:53–63 (1962).

HESS, E. H. "Imprinting in Animals." *Scientific American,* 198(3):81–90 (1958).

JAY, P. C. "The Common Langur of North India." In *Primate Behavior: Field Studies of Monkeys and Apes,* I. De Vore (ed.) New York: Holt, Rinehart and Winston, Inc., 1965, pp. 197–249.

KLOPFER, P. H. (ed.) *Behavioral Ecology.* Encino, Calif.: Dickenson Pub. Co., Inc., 1970.

———— and J. P. HAILMAN. "Habitat Selection in Birds." In *Advances in the Study of Behavior,* D. S. Lehrman, et al. (eds.), 1:279–303 (1965).

LANCASTER, J. B. "On the Evolution of Tool-Using Behavior." *American Anthropologist,* 70:56–66 (1968).

MENZEL, E. W. "Naturalistic and Experimental Research on Primates." *Human Development,* 10:170–186 (1967).

MEYERRIECKS, A. S. "Comparative Breeding Behavior of Four Species of North American Herons." *Publication of the Nuttall Ornithological Club No. 2,* 1960.

TINBERGEN, N. "The Evolution of Behavior in Gulls." *Scientific American,* 203(6):118–130 (1960).

————. *Social Behavior in Animals,* 2nd ed. London: Methuen, 1964.

————. *Animal Behavior.* New York: Time-Life Books, 1965.

WASHBURN, S. L., P. C. JAY, and J. B. LANCASTER. "Field Studies of Old World Monkeys and Apes." *Science,* 150:1541–1547 (1965).

WECKER, S. C. "The Role of Early Experience in Habitat Selection by the Prairie Deer-mouse *Peromyscus maniculatus bairdi.*" *Ecological Monographs,* 33:307–325 (1963).

WOLF, L. L., and F. R. HAINSWORTH. "Time and Energy Budgets of Territorial Hummingbirds." *Ecology,* 52:980–988 (1971).

WOOLPY, J. H. "The Social Organization of Wolves." *Natural History,* 77(5):46–55 (1968).

Chapter 6 • Population Energetics: Organizing into Communities

Thus far, we have considered the nature of populations and the effect of the environment on them, their genetic origins, their behavior, and their interactions. This chapter examines the nature of the association that develops between sympatric populations that form interdependent assemblages within the same habitat.

Just as populations possess characteristics above and beyond those of their component organisms, so this association developing between populations that is described as a *community* exhibits characteristics above and beyond those of its constituent populations. These characteristics derive from the nature of this association between populations; they are one of the main considerations in the companion volume in this series on community ecology.

Food Chains and Energy

In a given habitat the individual interactions between two populations cannot be considered as entirely discrete activities. Populations that utilize other populations as prey may serve in their turn as prey for still other populations. An examination of any habitat will reveal one or more hierarchies in which a series of food-consumer, prey-predator relationships among resident populations may be identified. Such a simple hierarchy has come to be known as a *food chain*.

Energy passes from populations at one level of a food chain to populations at the next higher level. In terms of bioenergetics, each of these successive levels is known as a *trophic level.* The energy enters a primary or autogenic food chain as the radiant energy of sunlight, which in all but a few special instances is absorbed by green plants. These green plants therefore constitute the first level of the food chain, which then proceeds through a plant-consuming, or *herbivore,* level to primary, secondary, and even tertiary flesh-consuming, or *carnivore,* levels. This is a producer or autogenic type of food chain. There are also secondary food chains, alternatively known as reducing or detritus food chains, in which energy is obtained from chemical sources, that is, by the breakdown of dead organic matter. Energy transferred in this way through a food chain from one trophic level to another may be utilized in four ways. Some will go to *production,* the accumulation of what community ecologists describe as *biomass.* Some is lost in *respiration,* the oxidative process whereby the several populations in the food chain utilize energy for their various activities. Some is *exported* stored in living or dead organic matter. This occurs for example in the sea, where living and dead organisms rain down continuously from the euphotic zone to the deeper waters below. The rest is exported as *heat,* which is deliberately or inadvertently liberated during various activities.

Nature of Energy

Before examining the process of energy transfer between the several members of a food chain, it is first necessary to consider the nature of energy itself. Energy may be defined as the capacity to do work. It exists in various forms, but those of greatest significance to living organisms are mechanical, chemical, radiant, and heat energy. There are two forms of *mechanical energy:* potential energy and kinetic energy. *Potential energy* is stored energy that is only utilizable when it is converted into free energy to do work. *Kinetic energy* is free energy, that is, the energy associated with a body in motion, and it is measured by the work done in bringing the body to rest. The conversion of potential energy into kinetic energy involves the imparting of motion.

The source of the energy required by all living organisms is the *chemical energy* of their food. This chemical energy is converted into potential energy by the arrangement of the constituent atoms of food in a particular manner and is released as kinetic energy by a rearrangement of these atoms.

Chemical energy is obtained from the conversion of the *radiant energy* of solar radiation by producer populations. This radiant energy is in the form of electromagnetic waves, which are released from the sun during the transmutation of hydrogen into helium. The particular wavelengths utilized are in the visible light range, which we call *sunlight.*

Mechanical, chemical, and radiant energy all are the result of directional, or nonrandom, movement of molecules. When any of these forms of energy is transformed in the process of doing work, a random movement of molecules results. This random movement of molecules, which by virtue of their movement possess kinetic energy, is *heat energy*. All biological processes—growth, reproduction, and so forth—involve the transformation of energy, which results in the formation of some heat energy. For example, it has been calculated that in the conversion of the chemical energy of the hexose sugar glucose to potential energy during respiration, no more than two thirds of the chemical energy is converted to potential energy; the rest is transformed into heat energy.

Energy Transfer

The movement of these various forms of energy in a food chain is governed by two physical laws: the first and second laws of thermodynamics. The *first law of thermodynamics,* also known as the law of the conservation of energy, maintains that although energy may be transformed from one form to another, it may be neither created nor destroyed. Thus radiant energy in the form of light falling on a green plant is transformed partly into heat energy, warming the plant, and partly into *chemical energy,* which is stored in the various chemical products in the plant; this part of the transformation is initiated by the metabolic process we call *photosynthesis*. The *second law of thermodynamics* is concerned with the conversion of energy from a nonrandom (mechanical, chemical, radiant) to a random (heat) form. It requires that nonrandom energy cannot be converted without some degradation into heat energy. Therefore when the chemical energy accumulated by plants as photosynthates is converted into kinetic energy by herbivores when they consume the plants, some degradation of energy will occur through its conversion into heat. Further energy conversion and degradation will occur similarly when the herbivore is consumed by a primary carnivore and when the primary carnivore in its turn is eaten by a secondary carnivore.

As the initial amount of energy introduced into a primary food chain in a given habitat is limited by the duration and intensity of sunlight, there must come some point along the food chain of the habitat when this initial load of radiant energy has been transformed and finally all converted to heat energy. At this point the food chain will have reached the *steady state,* in which the amount of energy taken into its biological system in unit time as radiant energy exactly balances that returned to the habitat as heat energy.

Energy Measurement

In expressing amounts of energy, it has been found convenient to base the energy unit on heat energy. The unit of heat energy is the calorie. The amount of heat energy required to raise the temperature of 1 gram of water 1°C is 1 calorie; 1,000 calories (cal) constitute 1 kilocalorie (kcal). The calorie unit is also used for the comparative expression of the other forms of energy, which can all ultimately be converted into heat energy for this purpose. For example, the calorific value of chemical energy can be determined by combustion in a bomb calorimeter, which will record the amount of heat energy released during the conversion. The calorie is the basic unit for the expression of energy value in ecology.

Energy Absorption

The quantity of radiant energy received at any one point on the Earth's surface varies with its location and the season; it is usually in the neighborhood of 5×10^8 cal/m^2/yr, that is, 500,000 kcal/m^2/yr. This is less than the total radiant energy entering the Earth's atmosphere, for some of this energy is converted during the evaporation of water in the atmosphere, some during the dispersal of dust in the atmosphere.

It is generally considered that 95 to 99 per cent of the 5×10^8 cal/m^2/yr actually received is immediately converted into heat energy as sensible heat or the latent heat of evaporation. Only about one half of the remaining incident radiation is within the range of wavelengths absorbed by chlorophyll and can be used by plants during photosynthesis for the conversion to chemical energy. Plants therefore convert into chemical energy only some 1 or 2 per cent of the total radiant energy the Earth receives from the sun. When burnt completely in a bomb calorimeter, animals provide a mean of 5 to 7 kilocalories per gram of dry weight. Plants vary in this respect much more than animals; they usually yield fewer calories.

Ecological Efficiency

G. L. Clarke has expressed the ratios of energy transfer in a food chain, starting from the radiant energy received, as follows:

$$\text{absorption ratio} = \frac{\text{absorbed light}}{\text{incident light}}$$

$$\text{assimilation ratio} = \frac{\text{carbohydrates formed}}{\text{absorbed light}}$$

$$\text{growth ratio} = \frac{\text{plant growth}}{\text{carbohydrates formed}}$$

$$\text{increase ratio} = \frac{\text{net increase of plants}}{\text{plant growth}}$$

Combining these ratios, the ecological efficiency of the first element in a food chain, the plant, can be expressed as

$$\text{ecological efficiency} = \frac{\text{plant growth}}{\text{incident light}}$$

Ecological efficiency may be defined as the ratio of the energy used by one step in a food chain in unit time to the energy made available to the next step. Estimates of the ecological efficiency of plants generally lie in the neighborhood of 1 per cent. In the ocean, where much of the radiant energy is absorbed by water and by matter suspended in it, ecological efficiency in terms of radiant energy striking the surface of the sea is considered to fall as low as one fifth of this.

ECOLOGICAL EFFICIENCY UNDER LABORATORY CONDITIONS Ecological efficiency can be studied more simply and more intensively in laboratory experiments than in the complex situations of a natural community. In a series of experiments over a number of years, Slobodkin and his co-workers examined ecological efficiency under controlled conditions.

In the first of the experiments Slobodkin provided a three-element food chain comprising a green alga, *Chlamydomonas,* a herbivore, *Daphnia,* and a simulated carnivore, the people carrying out this experiment, who removed *Daphnia* to stimulate predation. The number of calories per unit time consumed by *Daphnia* and the number of calories removed per unit time by the experimenters were determined. The algal food supply for the *Daphnia* was grown on agar plates and fed every four days in a set ration to five different populations of *Daphnia;* every four days the first population received one ration of food, the second population two, and so on, until finally the fifth population received five rations at the same interval. The fixed volume of food that comprised a ration had been determined by bomb calorimetry to have a calorific value of 8.1 calories, so that assuming all the food supplied was ultimately consumed, its total calorific value could be determined.

At each four-day feeding interval the *Daphnia* populations were sampled, and the number and length of different-sized *Daphnia* were determined. It had been calculated also by bomb calorimetry that animals of 0.7, 1.3, and 1.88 mm length had mean average calorific values of 4.05, 4.124, and 5.075 kilocalories per gram dry weight, respectively, so that it was possible to calculate the total calorific equivalent of every *Daphnia* population in this experiment.

One control in which there was no simulated predation, that is, no removal of *Daphnia* by the experimenters, was set up with each population treatment, and this control population increased until it reached a steady state at the particular feeding level. The data from the five different control-population treatments indicated that there is a *linear* relationship between the energy content of a population and the energy content of the food consumed (Figure 6-1 **A**).

In those populations from which animals were removed to simulate predation, a number equivalent to a fixed percentage of the newborn young was taken. In some experiments young animals and in others

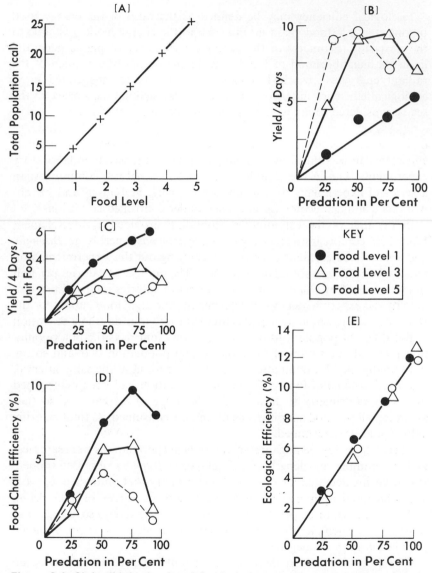

Figure 6-1. Slobodkin's simulated-food-chain experiment. A: Energy contents of food and population. **B:** Effect of different levels of predation on *Daphnia* yield. **C:** *Daphnia* yield per unit of food supplied. **D:** Food-chain efficiency.   **E:** Ecological efficiency plotted against level of predation. After L. B. Slobodkin, *Ecology*, 40(2): 232–243 (1959).

adults were selected for this purpose. The number of newborn young was obtained from the difference between consecutive population estimates. The populations chosen for the adult predation simulation were those given one, three, and five rations every four days. Four groups in each of these three populations were subjected to predation rates of 25, 50, 75, and 90 per cent of the number of newborn young, respectively.

It was thus possible to study the relationship between the number of calories of alga consumed in unit time by *Daphnia* and the number of calories of *Daphnia* removed in unit time. It can be seen from Figure 6-1 **B** that the highest yield of *Daphnia* occurs at the five-ration rate of food supply and the highest predation rate. However, the highest yield of *Daphnia* per unit of food supplied is something different. From Figure 6-1 **C** it can be seen that the food level with one ration only gives the highest yield per unit of food at all levels of predation.

The efficiency of the return to the predator of food supplied to the prey can be expressed as a percentage, as follows:

$$\frac{\text{calories of prey consumed by predator}}{\text{calories of food supplied to prey}} \times 100$$

This percentage is called the *food-chain efficiency*. For Slobodkin's experiments Figure 6-1 **D** shows the food-chain efficiency plotted against the predation rate; it would appear from this figure that *Daphnia* populations above a predation rate of 25 per cent had a reduced food-chain efficiency. However, it was soon discovered that these more highly preyed-upon populations were being "overfished"; not enough *Daphnia* were being left to consume fully the total food supplied. To obtain a maximum food-chain efficiency, the predation must be maintained at such a level that the food supply of the prey is fully utilized.

At this point a further percentage figure can be calculated, as follows:

$$\frac{\text{calories of prey consumed by predator}}{\text{calories of food consumed by prey}} \times 100$$

This percentage figure is known as the *gross ecological efficiency*. For Slobodkin's experiments, the ecological efficiency at different predation levels is given in Figure 6-1 **E**. It can be seen that in these experiments, so long as the *Daphnia* populations on the different food rations consumed all their food, there were no differences in ecological efficiency; also, the maximum gross efficiency obtained was about 13 per cent.

When the greatest food-chain efficiency is realized through utilization of all the food supplied to the prey, food-chain efficiency equals gross ecological efficiency.

Further laboratory experiments by Slobodkin with a shrimp-hydra-man food chain produced a figure for maximum gross ecological efficiency of about 7 per cent. He therefore suggested that under natural conditions the average gross ecological efficiency might approximate 10 per cent as a theoretical maximum. This is the figure that is now usually accepted for every level in a food chain except the first, which was not considered in these particular experiments. It is, however, an approximate *mean* figure; in some food chains considerable departures from this figure have been noted.

The fate of the other 90 per cent of the energy obtained by consumers (heterotrophs) in a food chain, that is, by the animals that comprise the herbivores and the primary and secondary carnivores, is varied. Some chemical energy is stored and converted into kinetic energy during locomotion. Chemical energy is also utilized for the metabolism and the production of body proteins and other substances. Some conversion to heat energy occurs during all these energy transfers, and some of the initial chemical energy supplied by the previous level in a food chain is converted directly into heat energy.

ECOLOGICAL EFFICIENCY UNDER NATURAL CONDITIONS   Odum gives the figures reproduced in Table 6-1 for ecological efficiencies at the plant, herbivore, small-carnivore, and large-carnivore levels in the food chains of three contrasted areas. It will be seen from this table that the ecological efficiency of the first level of the food chains does indeed correspond to the figure presented by Clarke; that is, it ranges up to approximately 1 per cent. These various figures for ecological efficiency are not, however, all comparable. The primary efficiency, that is, efficiency of transformation of radiant energy into chemical energy, is unique; such transformation does not occur elsewhere in the food chain. Primary efficiency of one food chain and another can be compared, but primary and other ecological efficiencies cannot.

ECOLOGICAL EFFICIENCY UNDER AGRICULTURAL CONDITIONS   By largely empirical trials, agricultural food chains have been made more efficient, first by reducing the number of steps in the food chain, thereby minimizing

Table 6-1. Ecological Efficiencies at Various Food-chain Levels

Level	Cedar Bog Lake, Minnesota	Lake Mendota, Wisconsin	Silver Springs, Florida
Plant	0.1	0.4	1.2
Herbivore	13.3	8.7	16
Small carnivore	22.3	5.5	11
Large carnivore	Not present	13.0	6

After E. P. Odum, *Fundamentals of Ecology*, 2nd ed. (Philadelphia: W. B. Saunders Co., 1959), p. 55.

the 90-per-cent loss that occurs with energy transfer between each element, and second by the use of domestic animals, which provide an ecological efficiency somewhat above the average 10 per cent. Agricultural food chains rarely contain more than three elements; common ones are alfalfa-cow-man, corn-pig-man, and sorghum-chicken-man. Hard-pressed human societies may be compelled to shorten the latter two food chains to corn-man or sorghum-man; this provides ten times the amount of human food but predisposes toward protein deficiency in the diet. Groups under less financial stringency can eat pork instead of beef. The pig has the highest growth efficiency of any domestic animal that is a common source of human food, in the region of 20 per cent. It can therefore be more cheaply raised than other domesticated species.

Limitations on Number of Steps in Food Chains

The number of successive steps in a food chain is small, being restricted by the ecological efficiency of the process of energy transfer between each of the steps and by questions of metabolic rate and body size.

The smaller an organism, the greater its metabolism per gram of living matter supported, that is, of biomass. For a given amount of biomass the *total* energy utilization of a large organism will be considerably higher than that of a smaller one, but the metabolic rate, expressed as cubic centimeters of oxygen per gram per hour, will be lower. It has been experimentally established that in animals the metabolic rate generally increases in two-thirds proportion to weight or volume; or, by another measure, the metabolic rate decreases inversely as the length of the animal. However, these general expectations are frequently modified, for example, when warm-blooded and cold-blooded animals are compared, and it is difficult to make comparisons between plants and animals in this matter because of fundamental differences in structure.

Food chains progress at their consumer levels from smaller to larger organisms because each successive carnivore must be more powerful than its prey and because, except where large herbivores have evolved without an associated predator, carnivores are generally larger than herbivores. The biomass of individuals at any level of a food chain is, however, also related to its metabolic rate. Smaller organisms usually have a shorter life-span than larger ones; they have a more rapid turnover. A smaller standing crop of prey is therefore required to support a given population of predators when the prey is small.

Table 6-2 illustrates a hypothetical food chain of the plant–deer-mouse–gopher-snake–roadrunner–fox type; it is assumed there would be enough plants to support a biomass of ten deer mice per hectare. In this hypothetical example the fox will be hard put to survive.

Figure 6-2 illustrates an actual energy-flow budget as determined for a plant–meadow-mouse–weasel food chain in an old-field habitat in

Table 6-2. Effects of Ecological Efficiency on Energy Intake and Population Density in a Food Chain

Steps in Food Chain	Calorie Intake per Unit Time*	Number of Individuals per Hectare
Deer mouse	10^7	10
Gopher snake	10^6	1
Roadrunner	10^5	0.05
Fox	10^4	0.0001

* A 10 per cent figure for this rate between steps in the food chain is assumed.

Michigan. About 1 per cent of the solar energy received was converted into plant tissues. The meadow mice, which were the principal vertebrate herbivores in this habitat, consumed only 2 per cent of the available energy. A further 10 to 20 per cent of the potential energy in the vegetation may have been consumed by plant-eating insects. The weasels, which fed almost exclusively on the meadow mice, utilized 30 per cent of the mouse biomass available. Of the energy actually taken up by each stage in the food chain, the plants used in respiration 15, the mice 68, and the weasels 93 per cent. This supports the suggestion that successive stages in food chains exhibit an increased utilization of the energy taken up. However, in this particular food chain, so little of the energy entering the system was eventually utilized in the conversion of weasel flesh that it would have been impossible for the habitat to support a secondary carnivore preying upon the weasels.

Because of this tapering off of available energy in a food chain, food chains rarely exceed five steps and commonly have less. In the *ecological pyramid* thus formed (Figure 6-3), the higher the step in the pyramid, the lower the number of individuals and the larger their size.

Marine habitats commonly support food chains with five members, as in the phytoplankton–zooplankton–plankton-feeding-fish–porpoise–killer-whale chain. In marine environments, as in land environments, large animals may circumvent some of the elements of a food chain. For example, the blue whale, having been adapted to feed on zooplankton, is the final stage of a three-member chain: phytoplankton–zooplankton–whale.

Figure 6-2. Energy-flow budget for a plant–meadow-mouse–weasel food chain. Data obtained from an old-field community in southern Michigan; figures in kilocalories per hectare. After F. B. Golley, *Ecological Monographs,* 30(2):187–206 (1960).

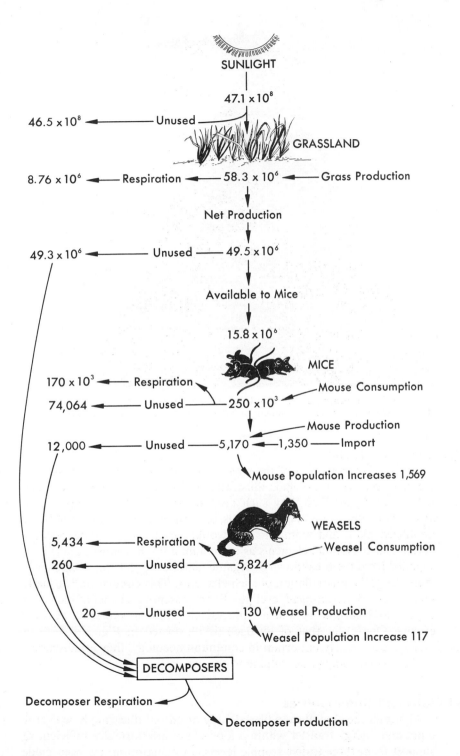

SUNLIGHT

47.1×10^8

46.5×10^8 ◄——— Unused

GRASSLAND

8.76×10^6 ◄——— Respiration ◄——— 58.3×10^6 ◄——— Grass Production

Net Production

49.3×10^6 ◄——— Unused ——— 49.5×10^6

Available to Mice

15.8×10^6

MICE

170×10^3 ◄——— Respiration

$74,064$ ◄——— Unused ——— 250×10^3 ◄——— Mouse Consumption

Mouse Production

$12,000$ ◄——— Unused ——— $5,170$ ◄—— $1,350$ ——— Import

Mouse Population Increases 1,569

WEASELS

$5,434$ ◄——— Respiration

260 ◄——— Unused ——— $5,824$ ◄——— Weasel Consumption

20 ◄——— Unused ——— 130 Weasel Production

Weasel Population Increase 117

DECOMPOSERS

Decomposer Respiration ◄———

Decomposer Production

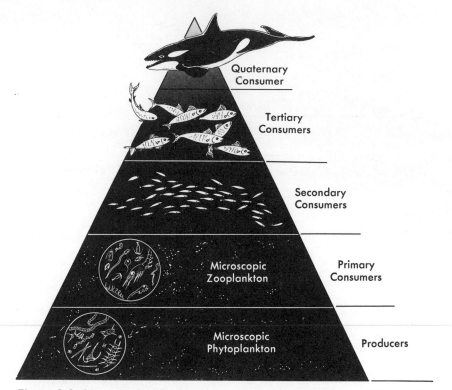

Figure 6-3. An ecological pyramid. The higher the step in the pyramid formed by the food chain, the lower the number of individuals, and the larger their size.

Biogeochemical Cycling

From an examination of the energy budget for a food chain such as the plant-mouse-weasel chain illustrated in Figure 6-2, two consequences will be apparent. First, any such predator-type food chain must have associated with it a number of detritus, or reducer, food chains; otherwise, unutilized plant and animal tissues would rapidly accumulate. Second, because such essential elements as potassium and phosphorus are largely supplied from the breakdown of organic material by detritus food chains, there has to be a circulation of such elements. This circulation is usually known as *biogeochemical* cycling. Every essential element, including oxygen and carbon as well as mineral elements, is subjected to such cycling. One cycle, that of nitrogen, is illustrated in Figure 6-4. Such cycles are extremely important in community ecology, they are discussed further in the companion volume to this work.

Food Webs and Communities

Although the several examples already discussed illustrate how energy input and energy transfer within a food chain are normally sufficient to support from three to five trophic levels, an assumption has been made

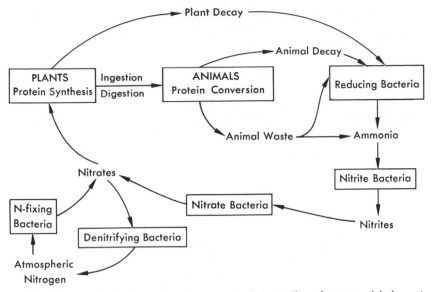

Figure 6-4. The nitrogen cycle. An example of the cycling of an essential element between a predator-type food chain a a series of detritus food chains. Such bio geochemical cycles are extremely important in community ecology.

that is generally untrue under natural conditions. Herbivores and carnivores rarely utilize only one source of food as they are forced to do in laboratory experiments or under agricultural conditions. Thus, an area of California chaparral that supports pack rats will almost certainly also contain other herbivores, such as pocket mice and several species of deer mice. Gopher snakes in the area will prey upon all these species and moreover will consume dead as well as living animals. Omnivores, such as opossums and raccoons, will sometimes behave as herbivores and sometimes prey on insects and rodents. King snakes may eat gopher snakes, but they will also consume any rodent they are able to catch and any bird's eggs or young that they encounter. Roadrunners eat many things other than snakes, and foxes do not stick monotonously to roadrunners.

Any given habitat therefore rarely supports a series of unrelated food chains. More usually there is an interrelated feeding complex of populations, conveniently classifiable as the plant, herbivore, and carnivore steps. Together these steps make up what is described as a *food web* or a *food net* (Figure 6-5).

The populations of plants and animals that compose a food web are linked by the interconnecting energy-transfer pathways of the web's interwoven systems of food chains. Besides these predator-prey relationships between the populations, there may be selective advantages in this association—for example, some benefit from modification of the physical parameters of the habitat; some from the development of such population

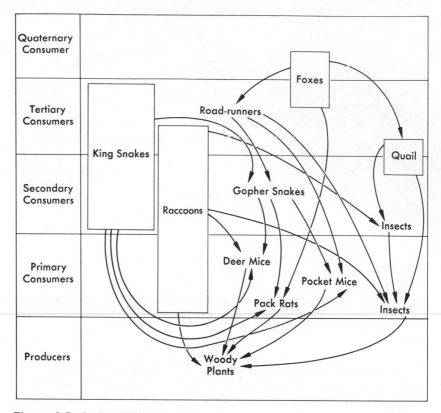

Figure 6-5. A simplified scheme of a chaparral food web. Arrows point to consumers of particular food and prey forms.

interactions as mutualism, which was referred to in Chapter 4; and some from the consequent regulation of population density, which could be regarded as a mutualistic condition. This elaboration of food webs is generally believed to confer stability on the ecosystem in which they are included. The theory underlying this supposition is illustrated in Figure 6-6. As noted in Chapter 4, relationships involving a single predator species and one prey population may contain some inherent instability. When there is more than one prey population available, there may be a density-dependent *switching response* from one prey species to another. Switching the predator from one prey to another not only tends to minimize fluctuations in its population density, it also avoids extensive depression of the prey populations.

The Diversity-Stability Rule

The tendency for stability in an ecosystem to be correlated with the complexity of its food webs is sometimes known as the *diversity-stability*

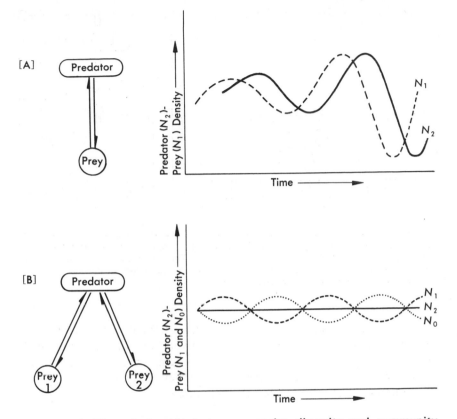

Figure 6-6. The relationship between species diversity and community stability. As illustrated in **A,** when a single population predates another single population, the situation is inherently unstable. If a second prey population is made available, as in **B,** prey switching will tend to balance any fluctuations in predator or prey densities. Partly modified from Wilson and Bossert, 1971.

rule. It is illustrated by the general instability of man-made monocultures. Modern agriculture tends to develop such monocultures, like vast landscapes of wheat or corn. They are very much exposed to disease epiphytotics. So are Arctic ecosystems, which likewise have low diversity. Tropical rain forest, by contrast, is exceedingly diverse and highly stable.

Diversity alone may not confer stability; it is especially a question of the nature of the linkage between trophic levels. In Figure 6-7 two ways are shown whereby four populations may be associated in predator-prey relationships. One system has twice as many links as the other and may be presumed to have a greater stability. Figure 6-8 elaborates upon this linkage theme. All four theoretical ecosystems illustrated contain the same number of populations. The first is relatively unstable because it has few herbivores. This situation might be found in a mangrove swamp or a corn field. The second likewise is unstable because there are few

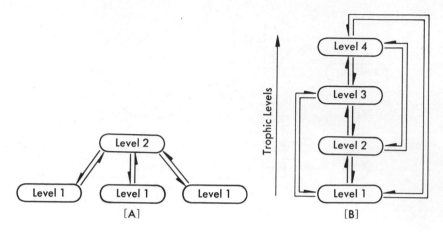

Figure 6-7. Food chain structure and community stability. Although the two theoretical food chains **A** and **B** each contain four populations, **A** has three links, whereas **B** has six and so tends to be more stable. The opportunities for the development of regulatory interactions have increased, as has the extent of interdependence. Partly modified from Wilson and Bossert, 1971.

carnivores, as on a ranch where such animals are considered vermin. In the third example the herbivores and carnivores are all specialists. Such a situation is not found in natural ecosystems, which contain many omnivores, feeding often at several trophic levels. This is the situation illustrated in Figure 6-8 **D** and also in Figure 6-5.

Diversity

In the introduction of the diversity-stability rule, diversity has been taken as the total number of species populations in an ecosystem. This is the sense in which the distinction between alpha and beta diversity is developed in the companion volume to this work. In terms of bioenergetics, however, *relative abundance* as well as species diversity has to be taken into account. Populations that are so rare that the switching response has already, at least temporarily, removed them from all but the lightest predation can play no significant energetics role in a food web.

The diversity measure most commonly used to express this required combination of diversity and relative abundance is the *Shannon-Wiener information measure*. This is similar to the entropy measure of thermodynamics and the information measure used in information theory. Further reference to this measure would take us outside the purpose of this text; a readily comprehensible discussion has recently been provided by Wilson and Bossert.

These assemblages of interdependent populations described in the last few pages constitute, as already noted, what are called *communities*. In the

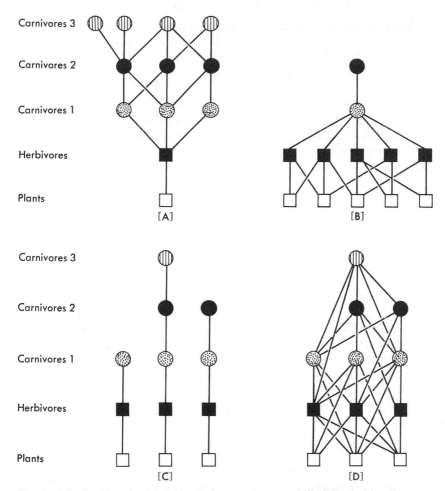

Carnivores 3

Carnivores 2

Carnivores 1

Herbivores

Plants

[A]   [B]

Carnivores 3

Carnivores 2

Carnivores 1

Herbivores

Plants

[C]   [D]

Figure 6-8. Food web structure and ecosystem stability. These four diagrams, A, B, C, and D, illustrate theoretically how with the same number of populations, ecosystems can exhibit a greater or lesser potential for stability. A has too few herbivores, B too few carnivores, C too great a predator-prey specialization, and D the greatest potential for stability because of the multiplicity of interdependent and regulatory links between populations at different trophic levels. Partly modified from Wilson and Bossert, 1971.

sense of bioenergetics, these communities must be composed of plant, herbivore, and carnivore populations, but the term *community* is sometimes used in a more restricted sense than this. Very frequently the term *animal community* is used to describe the assemblage of animal populations that occupy a given habitat. In this sense the various populations still usually have food-web dependencies, as well as mutualistic interrelationships. When the term *plant community* is used, however, the only implied interrelationships between the plant populations involved are of a mutualistic nature.

Some of the special characteristics of communities that are additional to those of the individual populations of which they are composed will now be briefly considered.

Spatial and Temporal Arrangements of Communities

The balance and the function of the populations within a community vary both in space and in time. Variation in space gives rise to the phenomenon of stratification, variation in time to seasonal and diurnal fluctuation.

Stratification

Communities that possess a large biomass usually exhibit stratification; that is, the populations they contain are spaced out vertically within the community in a discontinuous rather than a random pattern. A tropical rain forest, for example, contains two or three layers of trees; the emergent trees reach 70 or 80 m, in the understory the trees attain approximately 30 to 50 m, and the layer of smallest trees reaches about 10 to 20 m in height. Associated with this vertical plant stratification, but in some measure independent of it, are the various plant synusiae—the populations of epiphytes, lianes, climbers, saprophytes, and parasites. Related to this vertical and horizontal distribution of plant populations in a tropical-forest community are populations of animals—the bird populations, which feed in the canopies of the emergents but never penetrate below; the herbivorous mammals, such as lorises, lemurs, and squirrels, which feed in the intermediate layers of foliage, rarely descending to the ground or rising to the treetops; and large herbivores, such as peccaries and okapis, which feed exclusively on the forest floor.

This stratification of plant and animal populations is reflected in the below-ground portions of terrestrial communities and also in freshwater and salt-water communities. In cooler climates, where the communities contain a lesser biomass, they tend to have a more simple stratification among their populations, even one layer only.

Seasonal and Diurnal Fluctuation

The component populations of a community may succeed one another in time as well as in space. The most conspicuous temporal variation of communities is seasonal. Migrating populations greatly increase the complexity of the summer communities of both Arctic and temperate regions and of the winter communities of tropical regions. Seasonality, however, may take the form of replacement of, rather than addition to, the communities of an area. In tropical savanna regions with a dry winter and a warm, wet summer, dung is consumed by dung-beetle populations in the summer, by termites in the winter. The trilliums and other perennial spring herbs of a temperate woodland in the northeastern United States compete much of their life history in full sunlight before the tree canopy re-forms in early summer.

The distinguished British botanist E. J. Salisbury was actually the first to demonstrate such temporal separation of plant communities in a temperate woodland (Figure 6-9). He noted that as the year progressed, leaves and flowers appeared higher and higher in the woodland. The herbaceous rushes and periwinkle came into leaf and completed most of their reproduction in early spring sunlight, while frosts were still frequent. Bracken produced sori; perennial bushes such as blueberry flowered a little later, but still before full sunlight had been cut off from them. Finally the oak, mountain ash, and birch trees came into leaf and flower when temperature and light had reached optimal levels.

Local exchanges of populations in communities, similar to seasonal migrations but over a much more restricted distance, result from diurnal responses. The active daytime mammalian population of a wooded area may include squirrels and rabbits; by night there may appear raccoons, opossums, and wood rats. Generally speaking, butterflies move by day, moths by night. Swallows may feed upon diurnal mosquitoes by day, bats on nocturnal mosquitoes by night. These temporal relations between populations in a community, like the spatial ones, must be considered

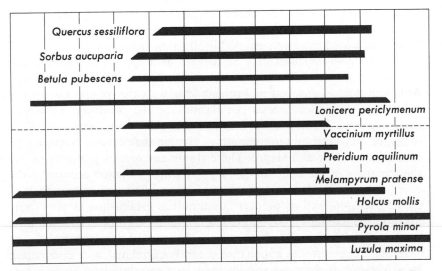

Figure 6-9. Temporal utilization of the habitat. Periods of active plant assimilation in a British oak wood are shown. The species are arranged so that the tallest is at the top of the diagram, grading down to herbaceous plants, the shortest of which is at the bottom. Note that the species of lower stature utilize radiant energy during spring and fall periods when it is not being intercepted by the leaves of the taller but deciduous species. After E. J. Salisbury, 1925.

in terms of the niche concept and the competitive exclusion principle, as well as in terms of bioenergetics.

Ecological Dominance

The populations of animals, plants, and microorganisms that together form a community are not all of equal importance in determining the characteristics of the community and its interaction with the habitat. A student might list the following species populations as present in chaparral:

Buckwheat	Pack rat	Pocket mouse
Sagebrush	Gopher snake	Opossum
Live oak	King snake	Raccoon
Toyon	Quail	Deer mouse
Elderberry	Roadrunner	Painted lady

Such a list would give no indication of relative abundance or importance. If, however, the cover occupied by the plant populations and the abundance of individuals of the animal populations were to be estimated, it would appear that sagebrush-buckwheat plant populations occupied more than 90 per cent of the ground and that by far the most abundant animals were pack rats and gopher snakes. This community could then be described as a sagebrush–buckwheat–pack-rat–gopher-snake community in which these four species populations constitute the *ecological dominants*. The removal of any one of these four species populations would entirely change the character of the community, whereas the cutting down of all the toyon or the catching of all the painted-lady butterflies would have no remarkable effect on the community.

An *ecological dominant* may be defined as a species population that exercises a major controlling effect on the nature of the community. Although it may constitute an intricate food web, the community usually contains one or two species populations at the producer, herbivore, carnivore, and reducer levels that are recognizable by the controlling influence they exert on the community, though they cannot invariably be identified by their abundance. These dominant species populations are the members of the community through which a major portion of the energy transfer is effected. Agricultural communities and communities of colder areas, as well as pioneer communities established in previously uncolonized habitats, tend to have few dominants. Tropical communities, on the other hand, tend to have a large diversity of dominants.

In plant communities abundance is rarely correlated with dominance. In a forest, a herbaceous species may be very abundant while a tree species is hardly so, in terms of the numbers of individuals present, but it is the tree species that determines the nature of such a community and is therefore the dominant. In plant communities the dominants are simply those plants that overtop all others in the community. In so doing, they modify the amount of light the subordinate species receive, the humidity, the amount of precipitation, the extent of air movement, and the composition and temperature of the air. Some plant communities have only a single dominant, as does a beech woodland in Europe or a black-spruce bog in Canada. More usually, however, there are several *codominants,* as in the mixed deciduous forest of the northeastern United States, the hard chaparral of central California, or the bayous of Louisiana.

Community Ecology

Besides possessing these unique features just described, communities have many of the same characteristics as populations. Thus, limiting factors and tolerance range, competition, genetic variation and adaptation by selection, and niche characteristics all apply as much to communities as to populations. In some situations populations apparently do not associate into discrete communities, but align themselves along the gradient of a continuum or in a catena pattern or form a mosaic by ordination. These and other phenomena and concepts of community ecology are discussed in the companion work in this series.

References and Further Readings

CLARKE, G. L. *Elements of Ecology.* New York: John Wiley & Sons, Inc., 1954.

GOLLEY, F. B. "Energy Dynamics of a Food Chain of an Old-field Community." *Ecological Monographs,* 30:187–206 (1960).

KOZLOVSKY, D. G. "A Critical Evaluation of the Trophic Level Concept. I. Ecological Efficiencies." *Ecology,* 49:48–60 (1968).

MCNAUGHTON, S. J., and L. L. WOLF. "Dominance and the Niche in Ecological Systems." *Science,* 167:131–139 (1970).

ODUM, E. P. "Energy Flow in Ecosystems: A Historical Review." *American Zoologist,* 8:11–18 (1968).

OVINGTON, J. D. "Dry Matter Production by *Pinus sylvestris.*" *Annals of Botany,* 4:5–58 (1957).

PEQUEGNAT, W. E. "Whales, Plankton and Man." *Scientific American,* 198(1):84–90 (1958).

PHILLIPSON, J. *Ecological Energetics.* New York: St. Martin's Press, Inc., 1966.

RISSER, P. G., and E. L. RICE, "Diversity in Tree Species in Oklahoma Upland Forests." *Ecology,* 52:876–880 (1971).

SLOBODKIN, L. B. "Energetics in *Daphnia pulex* Populations." *Ecology,* 40:232–243 (1959).

STEELE, J. H. (ed.) *Marine Food Chains.* Berkeley: University of California Press, 1970.

WILSON, E. O., and W. H. BOSSERT, *A Primer of Population Biology.* Stamford, Conn.: Sinauer Associates, Inc., 1971.

Chapter 7 • Human Ecology

Various references have been made in the previous six chapters to human populations. It will already be apparent that no more and no less than in any other species populations, our own populations have evolved by interaction between selection pressures and genetic variation. There have been in the past, and still are at present, both random and directional changes in gene frequencies. In addition to this evolutionary development, we exhibit, just as does any other species, such dynamic phenomena as natality, mortality, and natural increase. No more and no less than any other species do we exist alone in the world, but compete with other populations, and are inserted in various food chains and involved in a number of food webs. Although we are not usually preyed upon, at least not now, we are the host and the starting point, however unwillingly or unwittingly, of a variety of parasitic food chains.

In this final chapter, human populations will be examined in the light of the various concepts in population ecology that have been developed in earlier chapters. The extent to which such concepts appear applicable to our own circumstances will be explored.

Human Evolution

A convenient starting point for the investigation of the ecology of our own species is an examination of the degree to which it differs from and resembles other related populations. An analysis of human morphological and anatomical features reveals that in the possession of a placenta, three kinds of teeth (canines, incisors, and molars), opposable innermost digits (thumbs), two pectoral mammae, scrotal testes, a posteriorly lobed brain, and a tendency toward single births, our species can be classified as belonging to the zoological order known as *Primates*. In this order are also found the variously sized groups popularly known as the lemurs, tarsiers, lorises, tree shrews, monkeys, gibbons, siamangs, orangutans, gorillas, and chimpanzees (Figure 7-1). The first four forms, as seen from this diagram, are considered more primitive and are known collectively as the *prosimians*. The last three groups are commonly known collectively as the *great apes*. Together with gibbons, siamangs, and man, they are characterized by larger size, a tailless condition, prolonged parental care, and particular brain development; the gibbons, the siamangs, the great apes, and man are generally placed together in a subgroup and described as the *anthropoid apes*.

The primate order is characterized by features interpreted as showing adaptation to an *arboreal* life. Four separate and distinct living groups of primates, however, have adopted a *terrestrial* mode of existence—the baboons, certain other cercopithecoid monkeys such as the patas monkey, the gorillas, and man. The anthropoid apes are not uniform in this respect.

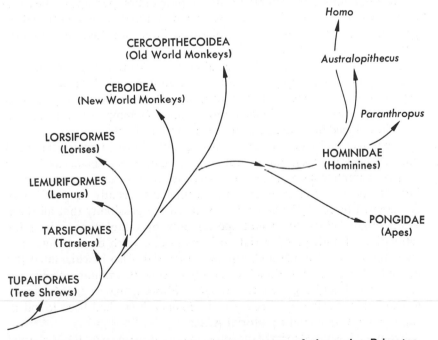

Figure 7-1. Relationship between various groups of the order Primates, indicating also the possible position of some hominid genera. The diagram indicates the relationship in time between the various primate groups, not necessarily any ancestral derivation. *Australopithecus* species are sometimes considered as referable to the genus *Homo*. Members of the ancestral hominid and pongid line may be described as hominoids.

Orangutans and gibbons rarely venture to the ground and may be described for all intents and purposes as exclusively arboreal. Chimpanzees spend much time feeding in trees but an appreciable period on the ground; gorillas may feed and roost at night in trees but are more terrestrial than chimpanzees. Man can still climb trees but is almost exclusively terrestrial. Interestingly, the ritualistic ready position of the American football player is replicated in the "knuckle-walking" locomotion uniquely displayed by these four groups of terrestrial primates, with the exception of the patas monkeys.

What induced these four different groups derived from arboreal primates to adopt a terrestrial habit is difficult to determine. Geologists have demonstrated that during the Tertiary Period, which lasted from 60 million to about 4 million years ago, the climate of the Earth was subjected to successively drier conditions. It has been determined from fossil evidence that, parallel with these changes, the essentially tree vegetation of the previous period, the Cretaceous, began to be mixed with plants of lower habit. During the Tertiary, such herbaceous forms as sedges and grasses start to spread. It is speculated that these new plant populations were not dispersed through existing forests but formed new plant communities in open places, developing at first perhaps in the form of grassy sedge swamp. Such new plant communities could be utilized by primate populations with wide tolerance limits for feeding sites and omnivorous food habits.

The first fossil records of terrestrial anthropoids that might have lived in and around such swampy communities are found in the African Miocene. Precisely when these terrestrial anthropoids, of which the best represented is *Proconsul* (Figure 7-2), divided into the *pongid* (chimpanzee and gorilla) and the *hominid* (human ape) stocks is a matter of debate.

A younger and less well-represented group of fossil remains has been judged to belong to a hominid that has been named *Ramapithecus* (Figure 7-3). No complete skeletal remains of these forms have yet been discovered, but the various skull fragments and teeth have recently been critically reexamined by R. B. Eckhardt. He explored the possibility that all these forms might belong to several species only by establishing a base for estimation of anticipated variation in skull and teeth dimensions from an examination of modern chimpanzee material. Also he calculated the possible degree of directional variation in time. Combining these two estimates and applying them to a range of Pliocene material, he was able to show that specimens all referable to *Ramapithecus* had been found in Italy, India, China, and equatorial Africa.

From the U-shaped form of the lower jaw, contrasting with the V-shaped structure characterizing apes, it is concluded that *Ramapithecus* is definitely hominid. It is actually the oldest hominid yet discovered, dating to the beginning of the Pliocene, about sixty thousand years ago, with possibly some older Miocene forms.

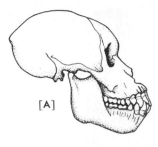

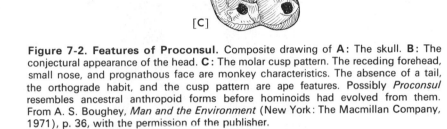

[A]

[B]

[C]

Figure 7-2. Features of Proconsul. Composite drawing of **A:** The skull. **B:** The conjectural appearance of the head. **C:** The molar cusp pattern. The receding forehead, small nose, and prognathous face are monkey characteristics. The absence of a tail, the orthograde habit, and the cusp pattern are ape features. Possibly *Proconsul* resembles ancestral anthropoid forms before hominoids had evolved from them. From A. S. Boughey, *Man and the Environment* (New York: The Macmillan Company, 1971), p. 36, with the permission of the publisher.

Figure 7-3. Comparison of dentition of *Ramapithecus* with that of other anthropoids. A: Capuchin (*Cebus*). **B:** Orangutan (*Pongo*). **C:** *Ramapithecus.* **D:** Man. All are scaled so as to reduce to the same length. The U-shaped arc in the capuchin and orangutan contrasts distinctly with the curved arc of *Ramapithecus* and man. This can be considered as supporting the contention that *Ramapithecus* is the oldest ancestral hominid known and a distinct genus from *Proconsul.* The lack of conspicuous canines suggests one of three possibilities: *Ramapithecus* was essentially an arboreal form, it lacked troop dominance hierarchies, or it was able to defend itself with artifacts. See text for further explanation. From A. S. Boughey, *Man and the Environment* (New York: The Macmillan Company, 1971), p. 48, with the permission of the publisher.

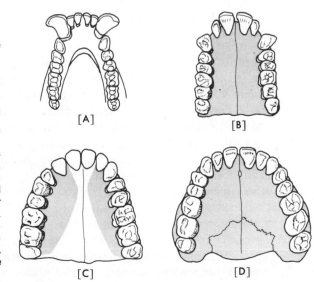

[A]

[B]

[C]

[D]

Figure 7-4. *Paranthropus* **male and female.** The stature is upright and locomotion bipedal, teeth large, causing prognathy, but canines not exceeding the length of the other teeth, brains about the size of a modern gorilla. Total weight was probably about an average 140 pounds in mature males, somewhat less in females; skin color, black. Time period about 2 million years BP, distribution, Old World tropics. From A. S. Boughey, *Man and the Environment* (New York: The Macmillan Company, 1971), p. 64, based on Matternes, 1965, with the permission of the publisher.

Still further argument centers around the characters that distinguish the evolving pongid and hominid stocks. Evidence from paleontology, archaeology, and modern behavioral studies suggests that both stocks exhibited tool-using tendencies and that both developed predatory groups as well as herbivorous ones. Nevertheless, it is only among hominids that extensive tool utilization has been employed to assist predation. One school of thought, as described by the novelist Robert Ardrey, maintains that it was aggressive predation, extending to feeding upon other anthropoid forms, that provided directional selection within hominids and culminated in the unique survival of a still murderous *Homo sapiens*. Another theory proposes that competition in Africa between two omnivorous groups of hominids where they were sympatric led to character displacement, producing on the one hand a largely carnivorous tool-making line whose members can be placed in the genus *Homo*, on the

Figure 7-5. (*Homo*) *Australopithecus africanus* male, female, and infant, contemporary and sympatric with *Paranthropus* illustrated in Figure 7-4. Similar upright stature and bipedalism, black skin pigment, hairiness, prognathy and large teeth, but with less massive jaws and slighter stature, averaging about 100 pounds. Tool-using; shown here bashing bones with stones so as to permit extraction of bone marrow, but little different from *Paranthropus* in this respect. Time period the same, about 2 million BP, distribution also Old World. From A. S. Boughey, *Man and the Environment* (New York: The Macmillan Company, 1971), p. 65, based on Matternes, 1965, with the permission of the publisher.

other an essentially vegetarian non-tool-making group generally included within the genus *Paranthropus* (Figures 7-4 and 7-5).

However this may be, the Pleistocene Period, which is now generally considered as having begun 4 million years ago, has been shown by increasingly intensified fossil studies to have been a time when hominids existed over an extensive area in a variety of forms. Broom and Dart in South Africa, J. D. Clark in Central Africa, and L. S. B. Leakey in East Africa have demonstrated a widespread African occurrence. Their work is supplemented by other discoveries pointing to a hominid distribution reaching not only over most of the African continent but also across the Old World tropics to Java and even China. These workers and others, such as W. D. Le Gros Clark and J. T. Robinson, have patiently and carefully attempted to interpret these scattered finds and relate them in a hypothetical account of human evolution.

From an examination of these fossils it is concluded that hominids had an upright carriage, were therefore essentially terrestrial, and were associated usually, but not invariably, with a tool-making industry (Figure 7-5). Some at least have been considered sufficiently human to be placed in the same genus as modern man, under such names as *Homo erectus* and *H. habilis.* How our own species, *Homo sapiens,* is related to these Pleistocene forms may yet be more conclusively determined with further fossil finds and interpretations. It seems likely that our particular species population evolved during the Late Pleistocene, which persisted until an estimated thirty thousand years ago. Estimates of the age of *H. sapiens* cannot be put much closer at present than between about 100,000 and 250,000 B.P. At least one other hominine species or subspecies population is known to have occurred extensively at this time—Neanderthal man. Evidence from a Mediterranean fossil site has provoked speculation that the ancestral population of modern man and the population of Neanderthal man were to some extent sympatric. Neanderthal man disappeared at the end of the ice ages, and the hominine populations remaining thereafter are all referable to one morphological species, *Homo sapiens,* which also constitutes a species population on a genetic basis as defined in the first chapter of this book.

The course of evolution in *Homo sapiens* presented briefly here has been based essentially on a detailed and critical examination of fossil skeletal remains. Inevitably this examination has placed an emphasis on two particular aspects of that evolution—locomotion and manual dexterity. Although the locomotor change undoubtedly provided unique evolutionary opportunities, this emphasis nevertheless tends to ignore the principal feature of primates, which they also display in a varying degree— *intelligence.* For purposes of comparison among fossil groups, intelligence is measured by cranial capacity (Figure 7-6). This can be interpolated from living groups, which provide data such as those listed in Table 7-1 for brain weight. Robinson considers that facility in the manufacture of tools for specific purposes would develop when brain size evolved to a volume between 800 and 1,000 cubic centimeters (cm^3), that is, about that estimated for *Homo erectus* in Table 7-2.

Cranial capacity, as indicated by brain volume, has been used by D. E. Jerison to calculate the total number of neurons in the cerebral cortex of the brain. This he takes, after allowing for estimated body weight, as a measure of the *adaptive capacity* of an animal. Table 7-2 shows the figures for the so-called adaptive neurons that he calculated for some primates and other animals.

Jerison's data in Table 7-2 suggest that on the basis of the number of adaptive neurons per unit of body weight, *Homo (Australopithecus) africanus* and *H. erectus,* tool users and probably both tool makers, were

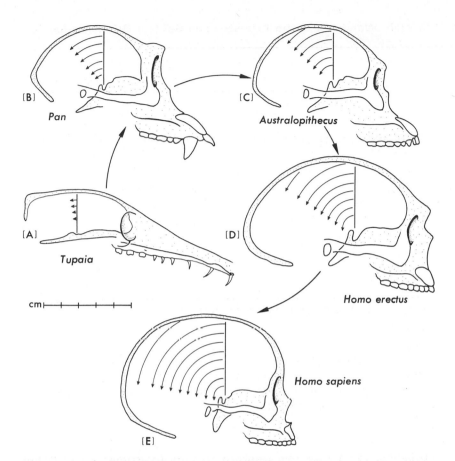

Figure 7-6. Cranial capacity contrasted. A: A tree shrew (*Tupaia*). **B:** A chimpanzee (*Pan*). **C:** *Australopithecus*. **D:** *Homo erectus*. **E:** *Homo sapiens*. The shaded section indicates the estimated position of the neopalliam, the part of the brain controlling mental reactions and willed movements. All sections are drawn to the same scale except that of *Tupaia*, which is four times that of the others. After J. Biegert. Reprinted from Sherwood L. Washburn, editor, *Classification and Human Evolution*, pp. 120, 130 (Chicago: Aldine Publishing Company, 1963); copyright © 1963 by Wenner-Gren Foundation for Anthropological Research, Inc. Reprinted by permission of the author and Aldine Publishing Company.

more adaptive than the modern chimpanzee and that *Homo sapiens* is by far the most adaptive animal.

Intelligence is an expression for a quality that is difficult to measure and compare even among contemporary human groups. It cannot be directly related to such features as adaptive neurons or cranial capacity. Although the evolution of *Homo sapiens* has been accompanied by a change in locomotion, a great increase in manual dexterity and acuteness of day vision, and the development of speech and language and a high facility for symbolism and the association of independent ideas, there is not necessarily any deterministic link between these several features. One

Table 7-1. Brain Weight in Living Primates and Several Other Mammals

Animal	Brain Weight in Grams	Brain-Body Weight Ratio
Primates		
Man (average 35 individuals)	1,308	1/47
Chimpanzee	325–440	1/129 to 1/135
Night monkey	110–120	1/75 to 1/84
Sykes monkey	60	1/81
Vervet monkey	61	1/65
Capuchin monkey	72	1/43
Galago	5	1/40
Other Mammals		
Deer	210	1/310
Bushbuck	140	1/253
Beaver	30	1/197
Norway rat	2	1/122

Modified from J. Buettner-Janusch, *Origins of Man* (New York: John Wiley & Sons, Inc., 1966), p. 351.

possible unitary factor in human evolution may have been the selective value of advances in data processing—the assembling, sorting, storage, and association of information—and decision making on this basis on a previously unprecedented scale.

Table 7-2. Estimates of Adaptive Neurons in Various Primates and Other Mammals

Animal	Brain Weight in Grams	Body Weight in Kilograms	Number of Adaptive Neurons in Billions
Macaque (*Macaca*)	100	10	1.2
Baboon (*Papio*)	200	20	2.1
Chimpanzee (*Pan troglodytes*)	400	45	3.4
Gorilla (*Pan gorilla*)	600	250	3.6
Australopithecus	500	20	4.4
Homo erectus	900	50	6.4
Man (*Homo sapiens*)	1,300	60	8.5
Elephant (*Loxodonta*)	6,000	7,000	18.0
Porpoise (*Phocaena*)	1,750	150	10.0

Modified from J. Buettner-Janusch, *Origins of Man* (New York: John Wiley & Sons, Inc., 1966), p. 350.

Language

In this process of mental evolution and its associated cultural developments, language must have played a unique role. Indeed, *speech* is the only characteristic which is a uniquely qualitative diagnostic of the genus *Homo*. The other features such as tool-using which have been mentioned before are characteristics in which we differ only quantitatively from other primates. Some other animals may be able to mimic a few words of speech, and even learn to associate these with particular objects or actions, but these would appear all to fall within the definition of behavior developed by conditioning.

Other primates use a call system rather than a language. The two differ in that the first is a *closed,* the second an *open* system. Among contemporary anthropoids, gibbons and siamangs have the most elaborate call system. The means by which such a closed system may be transformed into a language suitable for use with speech has been described by such authors as Hockett and Ascher.

The possession of a more sophisticated speech and language pattern must have had a very high selection value. Social organizations of family units, hunter-gathering bands, and finally permanent settlements would be much more effective when this means of conveying stored information was evolved. Variations in the efficiency of the cerebral lobes of the brain, which permitted improvement in the effectiveness of speech information transfer would then have likewise to be highly favored by natural selection.

Variation Among Human Populations

Our species as it occurs today is patently very variable in morphological characters but somewhat less so in physiological tolerance ranges and mental characteristics insofar as they have been, or can be, measured. On a morphological basis our species has been classified into segments of varying degree and extent. Basically all such classifications recognize three principal morphological subgroups: *Negroid, Caucasoid,* and *Mongoloid* (Figure 7-7). These subgroups, which are not all-inclusive, to a large degree coincide with subdivision on other bases, such as blood types. When the geographical distribution of these subgroups is examined, the possibility is raised that they developed independently from more or less isolated segments of the ancestral *Homo erectus* population (Figure 7-8) by parallel evolution from a *H. erectus* to a *H. sapiens* grade.

Cutting across this morphological subdivision are a range of characters that appear to be adaptations developing as a result of environmental pressures or, in some instances, as a result of sexual selection. Steatopygia, sometimes called the Hottentot bulge, is a characteristic said to have resulted from sexual selection. Perhaps the thick lips of Negroids have resulted from a similar process. Examples of features believed to be adaptations resulting from environmental pressures are the extent of

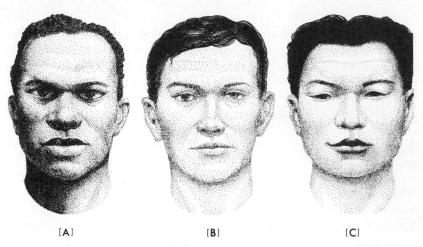

[A]　　　　　　　　　[B]　　　　　　　　　[C]

Figure 7-7. Facial form of the three generally recognized morphological subgroups of the species *Homo sapiens*. A: Negroid, characterized especially by small ears, frizzy hair, and thick lips. **B:** Caucasoid, characterized by medium to large ears, straight or wavy hair, and thin lips. **C:** Mongoloid, characterized by medium-sized ears, straight coarse hair, thin lips, and a fold of fatty tissue in the upper eyelids.

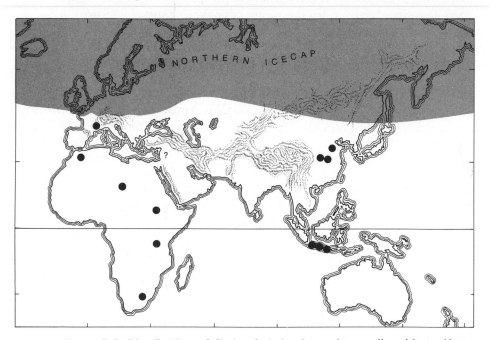

Figure 7-8. Distribution of finds of skeletal remains attributable to *Homo erectus*. Shaded area indicates position of polar ice sheet and European alpine glaciation about 500,000 BP, which is the approximate date for many of these finds. By contrast with *Paranthropus, Homo africanus,* and *H. habilis,* remains of which have not been found outside tropical areas, *H. erectus* could exist in a wide range of climates, from tropical to Arctic. From A. S. Boughey, *Man and the Environment* (New York: The Macmillan Company, 1971), p. 110, with the permission of the publisher.

pigmentation in the epidermis, hair, and eyes, size of teeth and extent of prognathy, nasal spread and height, body size and shape, and body size in proportion to the extremities. The relationships between some of these traits and the environment, which hold true whichever of the main sub-groups is under consideration, have been expressed in two general rules. Before considering these, however, it is necessary to examine the extent of phenotypic variation in *Homo sapiens*.

Phenotypic Variation

The occasional occurrence of human multiple births provides an opportunity for analytic observation of environment-selected variation on certain characters, or traits, that are otherwise genetically determined. The variation between monozygotic, or identical, twins (that is, twins originating from the same fertilized ovum) may be compared with that between dizygotic, or fraternal, twins. Also, the variation between identical twins raised together may be compared with the variation between identical twins raised separately under different environmental conditions.

Table 7-3. Coefficients of Heritability of Traits in Identical and Fraternal Twins

	Heritability Coefficient	
Trait	Males	Females
Head breadth	.95	.76
Cephalic index	.90	.70
Sitting height	.85	.85
Foot length	.85	.82
Arm length	.80	.87
Stature	.79	.92
Waist width	.79	.63
Leg length	.77	.92
Upper-face height	.71	.72
Upper-arm muscularity	.68	.53
Thigh length	.65	.68
Head circumference	.63	.70
Chest breadth	.54	.55
Mouth width	.46	.64
Chest depth	.45	.17
Weight	.05	.42
Bizygomatic breadth	.00	.68
Head length	.00	.58

After R. H. Osborne and F. V. DeGeorge, *Genetic Basis of Morphological Variation* (Cambridge: Harvard University Press and The Commonwealth Fund, 1959).

From the first comparison, made in Table 7-3, it would appear that there is a high *coefficient of heritability* in such traits as head breadth, cephalic index, stature, and arm length; in other words, there is relatively little combined phenotypic and genotypic variation in these traits. Considerable variation was observed in weight, in chest depth, and between the sexes. This variation could have arisen as either genotypic or phenotypic variation, or both. The question of genotypic or phenotypic variation or both may be resolved to some extent by observations made when monozygotic twins have been raised independently (Table 7-4).

Apart from the data for weight, the figures in Table 7-4 agree fairly well with comparable data in Table 7-3; they suggest that morphological characters, such as stature and sitting height, show some genetic variation in human populations but are little subject to phenotypic variation. On the other hand, some of the variation shown in mental attributes may result from interaction with the environment during development, that is, may be phenotypic variation.

Such phenotypic variation during development is irreversible. Other phenotypic variation, especially in physiological characters, can be reversible. This reversible adaptation to environmental requirements, noted in Chapter 3, is known as *acclimation*. Human populations can adjust their physiology and behavior within certain limits in a reversible manner in response to changes in oxygen pressure, to high and low temperatures, to varying times of onset of day and night, and to the amount of work they perform.

Table 7-4. Coefficients of Heritability in Fraternal Twins and Identical Twins Raised Separately and Together

Trait	Fraternal Twins	Identical Twins		Heritability Coefficient
		Reared Together	Reared Apart	
Stature	.54	.93	.97	.81
Sitting height	.50	.88	.96	.76
Weight	.63	.92	.89	.78
Binet mental age	.60	.86	.64	.65
Binet IQ	.63	.88	.67	.68
Otis IQ	.62	.92	.73	.80

Modified from *Twins: A Study of Heredity and Environment* by H. H. Newman, F. N. Freeman, and K. J. Holzinger by permission of The University of Chicago Press. Copyright 1937 by The University of Chicago Press.

Intraspecific Variation

Morphological, physiological, and behavioral differences not due to phenotypic variation are also found in human isolates. Two rules have been applied to account for some of the morphological variation. *Bergmann's rule* is a generalization postulating that as temperatures decrease from the Equator toward the poles, the body shape of mammals and birds tends to provide a lower ratio of body surface to body weight; that is to say, the surface area is proportionately reduced. In human population variation, this phenomenon interacts with other tendencies described under *Allen's rule,* which supposes that across a similar declining temperature gradient, the extremities of the body tend to become shorter in proportion to trunk size.

These two rules together provide a plausible explanation for some of the observable variation in body size and shape encountered in human populations that is not attributable to phenotypic variation. Eskimos have shorter arms and legs in proportion to their trunk size, which is comparatively larger than in any other contemporary group. In tropical zones two departures are found from the general body size and proportions of temperate zone populations. Largely food-gathering groups, such as Congo pygmies, supposedly having a low protein supply, conform with Bergmann's rule by evolving smaller stature, thus keeping cooler by losing more heat than would otherwise be possible. Pastoralists, on the other hand, such as the African Nilotics, Masai, or Watusi, are not on protein-deficient diets; there is no selection on this account against a lengthening of the limbs under Allen's rule to increase heat exchange with the environment. These three groups of pastoralists, by virtue especially of their long legs and necks, are among the tallest of the surviving human groups.

The size of the teeth can be related to the nature of the food and the extent to which the mouth is used to assist the hands in manipulations. The size of the teeth, in turn, will affect the width of the face and thus of the nostrils. The height of the nasal bridge, with the consequent extension of the nasal passages, has been shown to have some correlation with the humidity and, perhaps more importantly, the temperature of the inhaled air. Although the amount of skin, hair, and eye pigmentation appears to be dependent on the intensity of the incident radiation, no completely acceptable explanation for this correlation has yet been presented.

Such morphological variation has been extensively investigated by physical anthropologists. It can be subdivided into variation defining morphological subgroups and other variation of more general occurrence responding to particular selection pressures. Differences in physiological and intellectual performance are more difficult to determine. Some qualitative differences, such as the blood types, are precisely measurable. Others are less well known and indeed can become emotionally controversial. Observations can be made, but their interpretation is difficult. For example, the mean brain size of Mongoloids is larger than that of the other two main human subgroups, but there is not yet any proof that this is associated with a significantly greater intellectual capacity. In the Olympic athletic events of recent years, competitors of Negroid origin have generally achieved better performances in the foot races over distances up to four hundred meters. In the human population as a whole, people of Negroid stock appear to show a greater sensitivity to tonal values and musical rhythms than do peoples from the other two subgroups. However, as in the case of physiological features such as blood groups, too much movement and intermarriage may occur in the human population before the physiologist, the psychologist, and the sociologist can record and explain quantitative and qualitative differences that may once have developed between particular isolates.

Breeding Systems and Gene Frequencies

Such variation as has been observed in human populations must have arisen at least in part at a time when breeding systems may have been different from the exclusive monogamy generally but not universally practiced today. Troop-forming primates have been investigated, and some comparison of their possible breeding systems with those of early man has been made. However, caution has to be exercised in so doing. Social behavior among primates not only varies between species, it is sometimes found to be quite contrasted as between a deme in one area and the other demes of the same species elsewhere. It is necessary to resist the temptation to select anthropocentric examples of behavior, and ignore those cases that appear anomalous. Summarizing a number of studies on social behavior in baboon troops, J. Buettner-Janusch comments that observations suggest a female is never monopolized by a single male, although it is possible that achievement of fertilization may be restricted to certain males in a troop. In other words, there is no permanent pairing in baboon troops.

Just as baboon troops occupy and defend a territory, so, it is concluded, would hominid groups describable as isolates. Within these isolates, gene frequency would be less related to the breeding system than to the occurrence of genetic drift and to the chance gene representation in what T. Dobzhansky called the *founders,* the individuals from which the isolate was derived. An allele that in the homozygous condition prevented an individual from reproducing would have a lower gene frequency in isolates having a harem system than in those having random mating if one of the founder males was heterozygous for this allele. Nevertheless, this allele could be eliminated from the population only by genetic drift.

As Buettner-Janusch comments, American Indian populations are assumed to have been founded in late Pleistocene times by nomadic hunting and food-gathering isolates migrating overland across the then-closed Bering Strait. The founder group or groups appear to have lacked the gene for blood group B, which is unknown in American Indians. An alternative explanation of its being unknown could be that phenotypes possessing the ABO blood group system were eliminated by natural selection, but it is not necessary to bring in genetic drift. Although random drift can eliminate alleles, as well as lead to fixation, it is more commonly held to *modify* gene frequency in existing human isolates.

G. B. Glass provides data on a small isolate of the Dunker sect. The Dunkers live in small groups that intermarry within their religion. The particular community examined was in Franklin County, Pennsylvania. Gene frequencies were estimated in the community and in surrounding American populations. Comparisons were also made with populations in those parts of Germany from which twenty-seven families of Dunkers emigrated two centuries ago. Data on a number of physical features, such as earlobe length and handedness, were obtained from three successive generations, but no significant differences were found. In the MN blood groups, however, the M frequency drifted upward significantly, as is seen in Table 7.5. Thus, one allele frequency can change by genetic drift while others remain stable.

Although it seems likely that hominids existed in small isolates, the breeding systems operative in them are not yet known and would appear from present knowledge to be indeterminable. Gene representation in the isolates would follow Dobzhansky's founder principle; gene frequency would be exposed to Sewall Wright's random-drift phenomenon. Gene frequency would be further subject to modification by the mating behavior and the extent of migration and outbreeding between isolates.

Isolate Size

The population size of hominid isolates can be estimated by comparison with surviving societies of hunters and food gatherers, such as the Bushmen of the African Kalahari region and the aborigines of Western and Central

Table 7-5. Analysis of MN Blood Groups Among Pennsylvanian Dunkers

Generation	Group M Phenotype		Group MN Phenotype		Group N Phenotype		Total Individuals
	No.	%	No.	%	No.	%	
1	12	28.6	22	52.4	8	19.0	42
2	34	44.8	32	42.1	10	13.1	76
3	48	55.8	30	34.9	8	9.3	86

From Table II, G. Bentley Glass, *American Journal of Physical Anthropology,* 14:545 (1956).

Australia. Both these groups, it should be noted, now occupy only a relic area of their respective continents and must be regarded as adjusted to survive under more severe environmental conditions than formerly.

The continent of Australia is believed to have contained approximately 300,000 people of an apparently early Caucasoid stock at the time of its discovery. Among these aborigines the smallest population unit is the *horde,* a family clan of some forty individuals. Mating normally occurs by the introduction of females into the horde from other similar groups. The effective breeding unit is the *tribe,* which unites a group of hordes in a common territory, a common dialect, and a common range of personal mobility. Although its size varies, the tribe averages about five hundred people and therefore contains about a dozen hordes. The territorial limits of each tribe are determined by geographical boundaries such as ranges, divides, and rivers and ecological boundaries formed by plant communities, microclimates, and the occurrence of surface water. J. B. Birdsell has demonstrated the existence of correlations between the size of tribes and the amount of annual rainfall and between the size of the tribal area and the amount of annual rainfall.

Food Chains and Food Webs

An examination of what are essentially Stone Age populations, such as the Australian aborigines, provides data not only on isolate size and breeding behavior but also on ecological efficiency and energy transfer.

An exclusively predator-type mode of existence was found until a generation ago among Eskimos (Figure 7-9). In their type of food web, man takes little or no food other than what he gets by predation; thus he behaves mostly as a secondary or tertiary consumer. A very similar position in a food chain is associated with the Masai people of East Africa. They feed on the meat, milk, and blood of their cattle and so are exclusively secondary consumers.

At the other extreme were the Shoshoni Indians, who are reported to have been seed and root gatherers for whom game was of little importance. In their food webs the Shoshonis occupied the place of primary consumers. A modern parallel in an agricultural food chain is certain Far Eastern peoples who exist solely by the consumption of the cultivated soybean.

It appears likely that early man inserted himself into individual food webs at several stages. Table 7-6 lists the diet of an Australian aboriginal population and subdivides the members of its food web according to three stages. This is a qualitative, not a quantitative, list, but it should be noted that in this food web man's principal role is as a secondary and tertiary consumer. This was probably the case in most food webs that early man entered. Plants were probably generally used only to stave off famine at times when hunting was bad; plant gathering was women's work, hunting men's, as among Kalahari Bushmen. F. C. Howell and

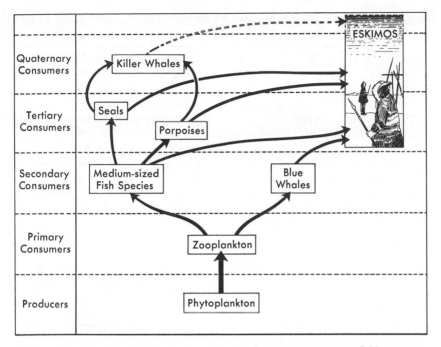

Figure 7-9. Predator-type food web. Until a generation ago, Eskimos were inserted into the Arctic food web exclusively as predators, being tertiary, quaternary, or even higher-category consumers. Now a significant portion of their food is store-purchased.

J. D. Clark estimate that in Africa some Acheulian hunting and food-gathering isolates took only about 25 per cent of their food as meat, the rest being plants. Nevertheless, the insertion of these later Pleistocene hominids as predators in the various food webs is held by P. S. Martin to have resulted in the extinction of numerous larger mammalian genera. The current term for this extinction is *Pleistocene overkill;* in Africa, Martin considered that about 40 per cent of the genera of larger game animals were hunted to extinction by approximately fifty thousand years ago. In North America, Indian hunting, food-gathering peoples are held by Martin to have had an even more marked effect on the diversified Pleistocene fauna of larger mammals, which survived here until perhaps twelve thousand years ago.

Population Growth

The population size of early isolates of our species population would always have been density-dependent, that is, limited by the availability of food resources. These, in turn, would be determined by environmental factors, such as climate, topography, soil conditions, and the isolate's

Table 7-6. Types of Food Consumption of an Australian Aboriginal Population

As a Primary Consumer	Birds of every kind including emus
Twenty-nine kinds of roots	and wild turkeys
Four kinds of fruit	Three types of turtles
Two species of cycad nuts	Eleven kinds of frogs
Two other types of nuts	Young of every species of bird and
Seeds of several species of leguminous	lizard
plants	Twenty-nine kinds of fish
Two kinds of mesembryanthemums	Four kinds of freshwater shellfish
Four sorts of gum	Four kinds of grubs
Two kinds of manna	*As a Tertiary Consumer (of carnivores)**
Flowers of several species of *Banksia*	Two species of opossum
*As a Secondary Consumer (of herbivores)**	Dingoes
	One type of whale
Six sorts of kangaroos	Two species of seals
Five marsupials somewhat smaller	Seven types of iguanas and lizards
than rabbits	Eight types of snakes
Nine species of marsupial rats and	
mice	

* An oversimplification for the purpose of tabulation. Some of this prey is to some extent omnivorous, and in relation to it the omnivorous man technically should be classified as both a tertiary and a secondary consumer.
Modified from J. B. Birdsell, *The American Naturalist*, 87:171–207 (1953).

degree of effectiveness in exploiting the food resources. From an examination of modern societies, it would appear that females are potentially capable of reproduction between the ages of thirteen and fifty-five, males from thirteen on for the rest of their lives. Gestation can occur at intervals as close as eleven or twelve months, and the occurrence of other than single births is a generally exceptional circumstance (about 3 per cent). In the human species population, therefore, each female is potentially capable of producing a maximum of about forty-two offspring, nearly twice what is the largest recorded actual number (twenty-four). Various factors must have intervened in preagricultural man to reduce drastically the number of births per female as compared with the potential. First, the age at death probably was about thirty, permitting the passage of less than half the potential reproductive life (Table 7-7). Second, a long period of nursing the young, as long as the two and a half to three years still found in some human societies, may have delayed the onset of renewed fertility and so the frequency of gestation. Third, there was probably a very high incidence of infant mortality among the recently weaned children, especially toward the end of the cold winter or of the long dry season, one or the other of which early human isolates had to endure, as discussed by Robinson.

**Table 7-7. Estimated Average Life-span of
Human Populations**

Population	Years
Neanderthal	29.4
Upper Paleolithic	32.4
Mesolithic	31.5
Neolithic Anatolia	38.2
Austrian Bronze Age	38
Classic Greece	35
Classic Rome	32
England, 1276	48
England, 1376–1400	38
United States, 1900–1902	61.5
United States, 1950	70

After E. S. Deevey, Jr., "The Probability
of Death." Copyright © (1950) by Scientific American, Inc. All rights reserved.

Although estimates of birth rates at these early times must remain largely speculative, comparison with some surviving hunting and food-gathering societies, as listed in Table 7-8, may be relevant. On the basis of such a comparison the average number of children borne by a female in Pleistocene hominid isolates was probably five.

Among populations in which modern medicine has not yet been extensively introduced, infant mortality may prevent approximately one half of the offspring borne by a female from surviving to reproductive age. Thus, it seems likely that early isolates of our species population were not subjected to rapid increases in population growth. Indeed, the balance of natality and mortality may frequently have been so critical as to have a very marked effect of both favorable and unfavorable selection on mutants attaining the homozygous condition. Individuals possessing alleles that were disadvantageous in the homozygous condition might die before reproducing. If these were females, this loss sustained over several generations would seriously imperil the survival of the whole isolate. At the same time, should the allele in the homozygous condition favor a higher rate of survival of infants to maturity, an extension of the life of breeding females, or some other factor causing increased population growth, this allele would have a significant effect on the size of the isolate. Its numbers would build up until it reached its ecologically optimal density; then it would tend to break off further isolates.

Judging from the quantity of artifacts that are found, it would appear that the dexterity for fashioning the skillfully worked stone tools of the life of Stone Age man was scattered widely through the population. It can be surmised that a high selective value would have been placed on

Table 7-8. Numbers of Offspring Borne by Individual Females in Some Contemporary Groups

Group	Number of Offspring
Food gatherers and hunters	
Central Australia	5
Western Australia	4–6
Tierra del Fuego (now extinct)	4
Hunters	
Greenland Eskimos	3–4
North American Indians	
Nootka	3
Chinooks	3
Omahas	4–6
Simple agriculturalists	
Orang Kubu of Sumatra	4
Ainus	3–4
Advanced agriculturalists	
Bantu	About 6
Nigeria	3–4
India	6–8*
China	6–8*

* Unconfirmed.
From J. B. Birdsell, *The American Naturalist,* 87 : 171–207 (1953).

such skills. Additional mutations that in either the homozygous or the heterozygous condition tended to increase such manipulative skills would confer particular hunting and gathering success on isolates containing such mutants. With improved weapons for the chase and tools for digging, these isolates could be expected to obtain more food, as happened when the modern Eskimo obtained rifles. The greater food supply would decrease the mortality rate, increase the birth rate, or both.

Permanent Sites and Agriculture

Hominid and early human populations thus existed for many millenia in the form of variously sized, migrant, hunting and food-gathering isolates. From a study of surviving representatives of such societies in the Americas, Africa, and Australia, it can be inferred, as discussed by Birdsell, that the average size of such interbreeding isolates was probably about five hundred men, women, and children. The effective breeding population of such an isolate, according to Birdsell, may have been 40 per cent, that is, two hundred individuals. Most of these isolates would probably remain fairly constant at this level. Some, through genetic or environmental mischance, would pass to extinction. A few would increase and throw off satellite isolates when a mutant allele developed that conferred selective advantage either in its heterozygous or, more usually, its homozygous condition. No general increase in population growth could occur with this mode of existence. As in the case of the Australian aborigines, population growth would be density-dependent. The number and size of the isolates would approach the carrying capacity of the habitat for human societies at a given level. Carrying capacity and thus population density would increase stepwise with each development that improved extractive efficiency. Although such statements must for the present remain largely speculative, it would appear that two circumstances vastly increased the carrying capacity for these early human isolates. The first was the establishment and occupation of a permanent site; the second, the adoption of an agricultural way of life.

The frequently commented-on effect of density-dependent factors on hunting and food-gathering isolates has been reviewed recently by B. J. Meggers. She concludes that in determining the level a culture may attain, environmental factors and their effect on the food resource are of greater significance than intelligence and access to, and receptivity of, new ideas. As regards the occupation of permanent sites, M. D. Coe and K. V. Flannery concluded that this was only possible when subsistence was available in a number of microenvironments close at hand. The establishment of settlements could thereby be independent of the development of agriculture and could occur wherever continuously productive food webs were available, as, for example, on the shore of a sea or a lake.

Eventually some of these early shore settlements must have adopted agricultural practices. Various modern techniques, involving, for example, the examination of feces that have survived in very dry areas or the estimation of the amount of pollen of cultivated plants in pollen profiles, are now permitting estimates to be made in various parts of the world that date the general development of agriculture in particular regions. With this development came the domestication of farm animals and the further selection of cultivated economic plants. It was no longer necessary for man to wander as a nomad over the face of the earth. By changing our level in the various food webs from that of a secondary or tertiary consumer to that of a *primary* consumer, we possibly increased, by ten times in the one case and one hundred times in the other, the carrying capacity of the habitat for our species population. This change would apply especially to the critical inclement season, through which previously we had to exist essentially and very precariously as hunters. The storage of plant food over the difficult season, whether it was a cold winter or a periodic drought, enabled both ourselves and our domestic animals to avoid the juvenile mortality that must have annually overtaken the migrant isolate bands. The effect that the avoidance of these annual juvenile losses must have had on population growth can be estimated from the present situation in a mammal with a comparable breeding system. Using the same example that Darwin selected a century ago, the African bush elephant of the savanna areas does not suffer significantly from any wild predator. A cow in its breeding life will normally produce some ten or eleven calves, but until recently elephant populations in the savannas did not exhibit any significant increase in population size. It is surmised that, during the six or seven months of the savanna dry season, increasing difficulty in obtaining water at all, and the necessary travel to obtain further supplies of water and food, fatally exhausted many of the young. The creation of artificial drinking supplies to attract and keep elephant herds in particular areas for the purpose of developing a tourist industry, has generally resulted in a massive survival of juveniles and a rapid rate of population increase, finally necessitating large-scale shooting of animals in an attempt at population regulation.

Urbanization

Between about eight thousand and ten thousand years ago, associated with the regional development of agriculture and the consequential increases in the human-being carrying-capacity of the habitat, came the foundation of cities in such areas. The urban life that is now a central, unique, and essential feature of our modern civilization had begun. The best-known ancient city, Jericho, has been excavated as far back as about six thousand years. Several other cities in this part of the Middle East, which appear to be two or even three thousand years older than this, have now been investigated. It is possible that as archaeologists labor patiently at their task, it will be revealed that about this time agricultural and urban societies were evolving contemporaneously in several regions of the earth.

The effect of urbanization on the rate of population growth was not at first always positive. The massing of people together made it possible for any disease or parasite to spread more rapidly than it could ever have done among scattered nomadic isolates. One of the earliest of such epidemic diseases recorded is schistosomiasis (bilharzia), the eggs, or cysts, of the causal agent having been found in Egyptian mummies. The schistosome worm, which is about one inch long, lives in various tissues of the body, causing extensive damage as its eggs agitate their way to the intestinal or urinal tract. This damage is debilitating and sometimes fatal. The eggs hatch in water to produce larvae that infect certain species of snail. Infected snails release microscopic motile forms that penetrate the human skin and develop into the worm stage. In Pharaonic Egypt, washing and bathing places on the Nile near cities would rapidly build up a level of infection high enough to ensure that a population using them would become 100 per cent infected with schistosomiasis.

Perhaps the most spectacular human disease recorded is bubonic plague, which swept over most of the known urban world in the fourteenth century in a form known as the Black Death. Bubonic plague is a virus disease carried by rat fleas. It is estimated that in one year, 1348, between one third and one half of the population of England succumbed to infection by it.

Thus, early urban societies may have overcome density-dependent regulation by the food resource only to have a further density-dependent factor in the form of epidemic disease impose restrictions on population increase. Not until improvements had been achieved in what may be called sanitary engineering was the danger of such a pandemic removed. Even in this century, there remains a group of bronchial virus diseases, popularly known as influenza, that could potentially regulate urban population increase unless modern medical knowledge brings it substantially under control.

The Population Explosion

The effect of removal of the two density-dependent factors of starvation and disease on the survival of breeding females in human populations must be stressed. Using 1950 population figures, H. F. Dorn estimates that 97 out of every 100 newborn white females in the United States will

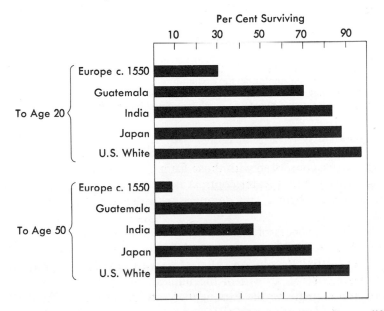

Figure 7-10. Mortality figures for females in various countries at different historical times. Survival estimates for Europe around A.D. 1550 are contrasted with some figures for 1950. Note the great differences between the figures for medieval Europe and those for all of the contemporary situations, although the latter still show a considerable variation. After H. F. Dorn, *Science,* 135:283–290 (Jan. 26, 1962). Copyright 1962 by the American Association for the Advancement of Science.

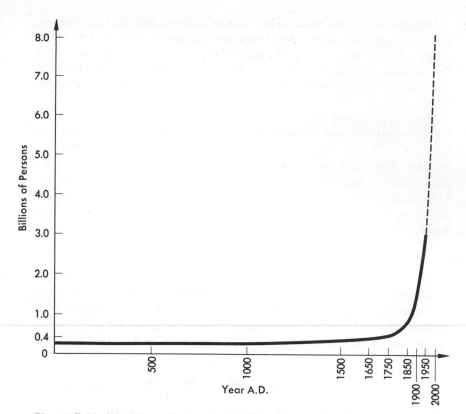

Figure 7-11. World population in the first two millennia of the Christian Era. Figures represent billions of persons. The dotted portions of the curve represent estimates of what may occur in the near future if present rates continue. The consensus of present opinion foresees a human population of 6 or 7 billion by the next millennium.

survive to age twenty—that is, to the beginning of child-bearing age— and that 91 per cent will survive through the child-bearing period. These estimates can be contrasted with those from Guatemala—70 and 50 per cent, respectively. Still greater contrast is shown in Figure 7-10, which incorporates these figures in a comparison with figures from medieval Europe.

The full consequences of urbanization on human population growth were not felt until the vast improvement in cultural efficiency that resulted from the Industrial Revolution. After this, with famine and pestilence largely under control, growth of the human species population could begin to approximate to the exponential rate discussed in Chapter 1. The calculated population size of *Homo sapiens* at various times during the first two millennia of the Christian Era is presented in Figure 7-11. As of this moment, as shown in Table 7-9, we are estimated to be doubling our population density every thirty-five years, and we cannot long hold ourselves down to this shattering but still modest rate of increase.

Table 7-9. Number of Years Required to Double the World Population at Various Dates in the Christian Era

Year	Population (billions)	Number of Years to Double Population
1	0.25	1,650
1650	0.50	200
1850	1.1	80
1930	2.0	45
1975	4.0	35
2000	8.0	?

After H. F. Dorn, *Science,* 135:283–290 (Jan. 26, 1962). Copyright 1962 by the American Association for the Advancement of Science.

The survival of a high percentage of females through their potential child-bearing years doubles the number of offspring that can be expected, as compared with presettlement populations. The survival of most instead of half of these offspring again doubles the population. However, this is not simply a matter of quadrupling the number of people in the next generation. Rather, the population increases by a huge factor, because, whereas formerly slightly in excess of an average of two children out of the five offspring per female had to survive to reproductive age to maintain the population size, now perhaps ten will survive. Instead of slightly in excess of four grandchildren surviving to reproductive age, there will be *no less than 100.* The total effect on world population is shown in Figure 7-11. In those parts of the world where voluntary restrictions on population growth are not in full operation, density-dependent factors of famine and disease still prevent the achievement of the potential rate of increase.

Population Regulation

It is sometimes maintained that our species is too recent to have evolved any mechanisms for regulation. Available estimates suggest that our species is at least 100,000 years old and perhaps a quarter of a million years old. It is therefore contemporary with the majority of animal and many plant species of the modern world which evolved in the Pleistocene, all of which when investigated have been found to have regulatory mechanisms. Moreover, there is some evidence, as has been mentioned, that we ourselves did have a regulatory mechanism in the form of a density-dependent carrying-capacity situation. Starvation was, and still is under some circumstances, a density-dependent factor; so is disease. What seems to be missing is a regulatory mechanism imposing an increasing environmental resistance before the food-resource carrying capacity is reached.

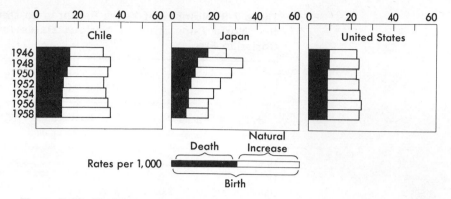

Figure 7-12. Birth rate, death rate, and rate of natural increase per 1,000 population for selected countries for the period 1946 to 1958. After H. F. Dorn, in *Science*, 135:283–290 (Jan. 26, 1962). Copyright 1962 by the American Association for the Advancement of Science.

V. C. Wynne-Edwards speculates that early human isolates did in fact have such a mechanism, and some kind of stress syndrome may now be beginning to serve as a regulatory mechanism. Moreover, social population control in the various forms that are generally categorized as *human sacrifice* have long been practiced, even by the earliest known forms of our society. Infanticide, especially the removal of female offspring, is one

Figure 7-13. Population structure. The human population age-group pyramids illustrated here and in the next two text figures have been prepared from census data. It is usual when census statistics are being compiled for such purposes to calculate separately the number of males and the number of females in individual five-yearly age groups. When these data are converted into population age structure pyramids, no more information is inserted into the system, but the various population phenomena become more readily observable, even to persons unused to analyzing such statistics.

The pyramids displayed here were constructed by the preparation of a computer model that would print out the pyramids when the appropriate census data were read in. One of the difficulties common to all these programs is that of equating the pyramid sizes when one is using data from populations of a widely varying size. In these programs the problem has been solved by the varying of the value of each population unit, measured by the scale at the base of each pyramid.

The two pyramids contrasted here represent **A :** a stable population, Sweden, 1967; and **B :** an explosively young population, Costa Rica, 1963. The population of Sweden is one of the most stable in the world, as readily seen from this pyramid. In common with all Western countries, the number of births in Sweden fell dramatically in the Great Depression of the 1930s, and this is reflected here in the lower numbers of the 30–40 age groups. The "baby boom" of the immediate post-World War II years, also experienced in all Western countries, is evidenced in the 20–24 age bracket. As females of this age group are the most fertile, this has produced an increase at the 0–4 group level. This does not necessarily mean that there has been an increase in fertility rates, but rather reflects the maturing of the females born in the post-1945 baby boom. Costa Rica shows an extreme case of a young population pyramid structure. As a result of the continuing high fertility rate of this young population, Costa Rica is currently estimated to have a doubling time of eighteen years, a patently unsupportable rate of natural increase. Programs prepared with the assistance of J. B. Pick and K. S. Wardell.

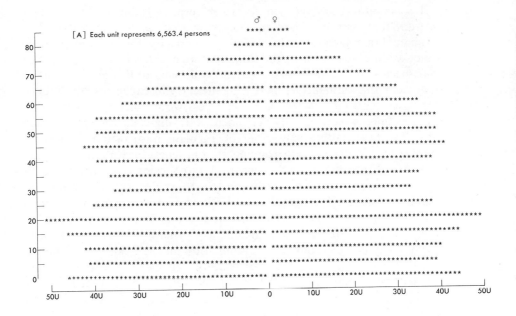

[A] Each unit represents 6,563.4 persons

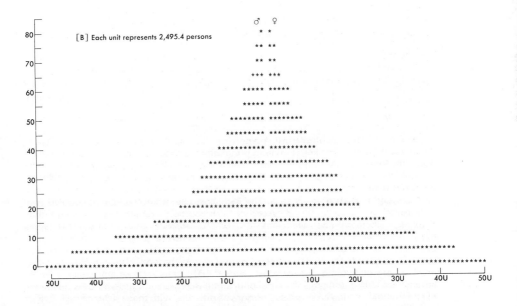

[B] Each unit represents 2,495.4 persons

such example. Ritualized killing of maidens or captives provides another, as does abortion within this specific context.

It was shifting our stage in the food webs, especially during the inclement season, that first increased the food-resource carrying capacity. The primate brain, greatly improved in its capacity for the independent association of ideas during the long hunting and food-gathering days of our species and its ancestors, was readily applied to the development of new techniques, still further increasing the carrying capacity of the habitat for agricultural and urban man. Nevertheless, we are once more inexorably approaching a new density-dependent carrying-capacity limit, which again must inevitably and unavoidably regulate the growth of our species population if current environmental and energy relations continue unchanged. The first time this occurred, our species broke the block by switching from being a predator and secondary or tertiary consumer to being predominantly a herbivore and primary consumer and by reducing competition from other species involved in our food webs through the adoption of various agricultural practices. This time there is only one further way in which our rate of population increase can be maintained without a voluntary reduction of natality—an increase in the carrying capacity of our habitat by the *chemical synthesis* of food. Although we are rapidly approaching the maximum ecological efficiency in the conversion of the potential amount of radiant energy interrupted by plants, if additional radiant energy were utilized to synthesize food or, alternatively, if the kinetic energy of radioactive isotopes were to be harnessed for the same purposes, our global population could presumably continue with its present rate of population growth for several centuries more. However, this could not be achieved without devastating modification of the ecosystems in which we live, as will be discussed in the companion work in this series.

Meanwhile, the biochemists have now produced the most sophisticated method for voluntary population regulation, which has been practiced at least since biblical times. This new method is the contraceptive pill,

Figure 7-14. The demographic transition. In 1939–41 and before World War II, Japan **(A)** had the same kind of young population structure as shown in Figure 7-13 **B** for Costa Rica. There was no decrease even during the Great Depression of the 1930s, because Japan had already embarked upon its colonial adventures on the Asiatic mainland. After World War II, the Japanese were evicted from the Asiatic mainland and confined to their home islands. The increased use of contraception, coupled with an accepted and widely utilized system of legal abortion, dramatically curtailed further population increase **(B)**. This almost traumatic achievement of the *demographic transition*, in which further population increase is prevented by the balancing of the birth rate with the death rate, temporarily halted further population growth. However, because of the "baby boom" immediately following the end of World War II, larger numbers of nubile females have now matured **(B)**. Even without any increase in the fertility rate, their presence will cause an upsurge in population growth, as is beginning to show in the first age class in 1967. Programs prepared with the assistance of J. B. Pick and K. S. Wardell.

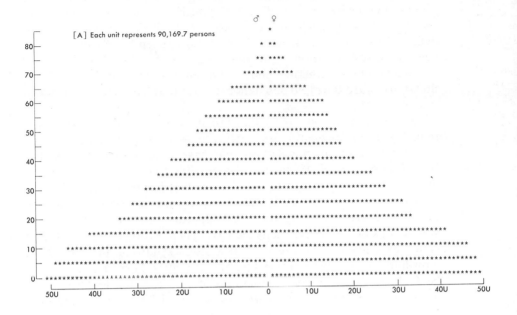

[A] Each unit represents 90,169.7 persons

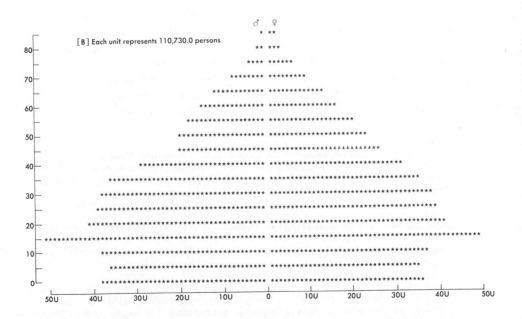

[B] Each unit represents 110,730.0 persons

a series of compounds that prevent ovulation and therefore conception. Associated with this have been still further improvements in the IUD, the interuterine device or loop. The use of such methods of contraception set our human species population apart from all the known ecological behavior of any other species. This ecological separation of mankind from the rest of creation began when we first abandoned our nomadic hunting and food-gathering mode of existence. At that time we took the first step toward the rapid population growth that has come to be known as the *population explosion*.

There is also the possibility that our increasingly crowded species is inducing the self-regulating *stress syndrome* very frequently encountered in other mammalian populations that have been investigated. As has been discussed by H. Hoagland, it is possible to argue the existence of an emigration urge in human populations that has been responsible for colonizing activities, at least since historical times began. It might be maintained that this emigration urge appears in response to a stress situation as human populations increase. There is otherwise as yet little actual evidence for the existence of a stress syndrome in man. Overcrowding is still a regrettable feature of many cities. There are reported to be, for example, hundreds of thousands of homeless individuals sleeping in the streets of Calcutta at night, but no parallel reports seem to exist of a diminished population growth among these unfortunates.

In the apparent absence of a definite stress syndrome or any other such regulatory mechanism in human populations, *we must voluntarily balance our natality rate against our mortality rate* at a predetermined stable population size. Assuming that we persist in our humanitarian endeavors to reduce the mortality rate, this leaves us with no choice but to lower the natality rate. We have now the technical means to achieve this even on a large scale, even for unsophisticated and impoverished populations. Some areas, the one most frequently mentioned being the country of Japan (Figures 7-12 and 7-14), have already adopted such a

Figure 7-15. Major variance in population structure. Various demographic influences may be observed in the U.S. (1964) pyramid **(A)** and that for Kuwait **(B).** The effects of the reduced birth rates during the depression years of the 1930s temporarily stabilized the population of the United States. As can be seen from this pyramid in **A**, the "baby boom" of the post-World War II years reestablished the pattern of a young population that prevailed before 1930. This was maintained through the next two decades. Only in the later 1960s did the United States population structure start to show a reversion to a more stable situation. However, as females in the four youngest groups shown here in **A** reach their most fertile ages, the population of the United States must again start to explode, unless these age classes show an immense and quite unprecedented decline in their age-specific fertility rates.

Because of its fantastic oil royalties when judged on a per capita basis, Kuwait (1965) is attracting vast numbers of young male immigrant adults, as illustrated here **(B).** There is no similar immigration of females on such a scale. The largely resident females have a very high fertility rate, so that the total population structure is extremely unstable and exploding. Programs prepared with the assistance of J. B. Pick and K. S. Wardell.

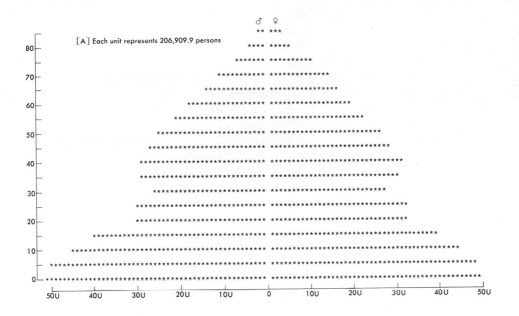

[A] Each unit represents 206,909.9 persons

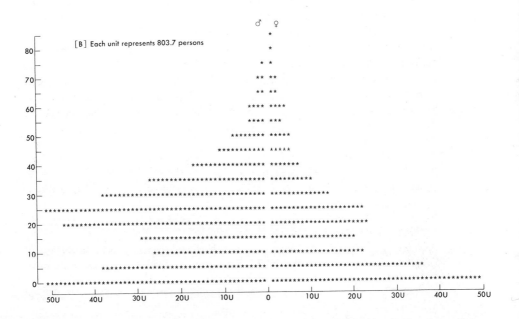

[B] Each unit represents 803.7 persons

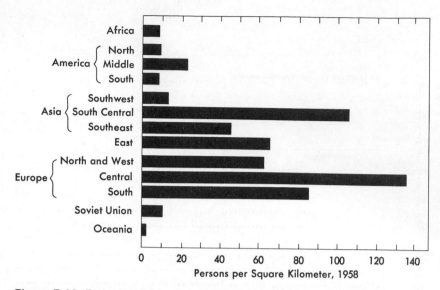

Figure 7-16. Estimates of human population density in various parts of the world from 1958 figures, expressed as individuals per square kilometer. After H. F. Dorn, *Science,* 135:283–290 (Jan. 26, 1962). Copyright 1962 by the American Association for the Advancement of Science.

procedure. In Japan an already accepted practice of abortion has been legalized and made more readily available. Together with a greater use of contraceptive devices, it is reported to have successfully prevented further marked increase in population size (Figures 7-13, 7-14, and 7-15). In a rather different manner, through delay in the time of marriage for socio-economic reasons, the natality rate in Ireland has been reduced and the population appears to have stabilized. Perhaps such isolated instances of population-increase control may inspire others to take regulatory steps, but time has almost run out for us. In some regions of the world, as depicted in Figure 7-16, it may already be considered to have done so.

References and Further Readings

BAJEMA, C. J. *Natural Selection in Human Populations.* New York: John Wiley & Sons, Inc., 1971.

BIRDSELL, J. B. "On Population Structure in Generalized Hunting and Collecting Populations." *Evolution,* 12:189–205 (1958).

BRACE, C. L. "The Origin of Man." *Natural History Magazine,* 79(1):46–49 (1970).

CASPARI, E. "Selective Forces in the Evolution of Man." *American Naturalist,* 97:5–14 (1963).

CROOK, J. H., and J. S. GARTLAN. "Evolution of Primate Societies." *Nature,* 210:1200–1203 (1966).

DOBZHANSKY, T. "The Present Evolution of Man." *Scientific American,* 203(3): 206–217 (1968).

DOLHINOW, P., and V. M. SARICH (eds.) *Background for Man.* Boston: Little, Brown and Company, 1971.

DORN, H. F. "World Population Growth: An International Dilemma." *Science,* 125:283–290 (1962).

ECKHARDT, R. B. "Which of the Fossil Apes of the Past 25 Million Years Was Man's Ancestor?" *Scientific American,* 226(1):94–103 (1972).

GOLDSBY, R. A. *Race and Races.* New York: The Macmillan Company, 1971.

HOAGLAND, H. "Cybernetics of Population Control." *Bulletin of the Atomic Scientists,* 20:2–6 (1964).

KEYFITZ, N. "On the Momentum of Population Growth." *Demography,* 8:71–81 (1971).

LEAKEY, R. E. F. "Man and Sub-men on Lake Rudolf," *New Scientist,* 56:385–387 (1972).

MARKERT, C. L. "Biological Limits on Population Growth." *Bioscience,* 16:859–862 (1966).

MEADOWS, D. H., D. L. MEADOWS, J. RANDERS, and W. W. BEHRENS, III. *The Limits to Growth.* New York: Universe Books, 1972.

MEGGERS, B. J. "Environmental Limitation on the Development of Culture." In *Human Ecology,* J. B. Bresler (ed.) Reading, Mass.: Addison-Wesley Publishing Co., Inc., 1966, pp. 120–145.

PILBEAM, D. *The Ascent of Man: An Introduction to Human Evolution.* New York: The Macmillan Company, 1972.

ROBINSON, J. T. "Adaptive Radiation in the Australopithecines and the Origin of Man." In *African Ecology and Human Evolution,* F. C. Howell and F. Bourliere (eds.) Chicago: Aldine Publishing Company, 1963, pp. 385–416.

STEBBINS, G. L. "The Natural History and Evolutionary Future of Mankind." *American Naturalist,* 104:111–126 (1970).

TIGER, L., and R. Fox. "The Zoological Perspective in Social Science." *Man,* 1:75–81 (1966).

TOBIAS, P. V. "Early Man in East Africa." *Science,* 149:22–23 (1965).

WILLIAMSON, F. S. L. "Population Pollution." *Bioscience,* 19:979–983 (1969).

Index

Entries in *italic* refer to bibliographical citations.